C000154575

# OLD TOOLS—NEW EYES

## *A primal primer of flintknapping*

### Bob Patten

STONE DAGGER PUBLICATIONS
Denver, Colorado

This book is intended to educate and entertain. The author shall have neither liability nor responsibility
to any person or entity with respect to any loss or damage, directly or indirectly, by the information
contained in this book.

Chapter-head illustrations are by Richard Jagoda.
Unless otherwise attributed, all other illustrations are by Bob Patten.

**Old Tools-New Eyes** Copyright © 1999 by Bob Patten.
*All rights reserved.* No part of this book may be reproduced or transmitted in any form or by any electronic
or mechanical means including information storage and retrieval systems without permission in writing
from the publisher, except by a reviewer, who may quote brief passages in a review. For information contact
*Stone Dagger Publications* P.O. Box 28018 #16, Lakewood, Colorado, 80228.

---

**Library of Congress Catalog Card  Number: 98-96919**

**Patten, Bob**
> **Old Tools—New Eyes, A primal primer of flintknapping**

**Patten, Bob, 1944-**

**ISBN  0-9668701-0-7**

# ACKNOWLEDGEMENTS

The writing of this book began at least 30 years ago as I tried to document my attempts to make stone tools. Full credit for gathering the bits and pieces into a whole goes to my wife Laurey. Her continuous support, encouragement, solid advice, and editorial assistance have kept me on track in spite of my wanderings.

The generosity of Dr. Dennis Stanford at the Smithsonian Museum of Natural History in sharing his collections and insight allowed me to tap the wisdom of past ages. Similar inspiration came from Alan Eichenberger and Pete Bostrom who tracked down and cast many of the master-pieces that beckon me on.

Thanks go to a growing network of flintknappers who continue to offer fellow-ship and show each other new limits to explore.

My final acknowledgement has to go to the master flint workers who have preceded us. It is not just the marvelous examples that have been left for our puzzlement and enjoyment, I am also grateful for the capacity we have inherited for making new and wonderful things, whether they are of stone or not.

# CONTENTS

# Chapter 1

# HANDAXES TO GUNFLINTS

When I was growing up in Western Colorado, my Grandpa would reminisce about how he had seen Ute Indians. One of the Indian boys that would run along the river on their way to hunting even gave him a small skunkbrush bow that graced the stairwell. Grandpa also talked about sites where Indians had scattered flakes while making stone tools with deer antler tools. What was a kid with a wild imagination to do? Clearly, the most direct action was to make my own arrowheads. Being only six-years old, there were no obstacles to be seen—all I had to do was saw off a deer tine from Dad's trophy rack and I'd be in business.

After a few strokes of the hacksaw through my finger I reconsidered my plan. This was not quite as easy as I had thought. The project lay idle for a few years, but certainly not forgotten. In high school I considered that an old nail made an acceptable and safe substitute for antler and soon my room was decorated with "arrowheads" crushed from thin flakes of chert. While I could get the right shape, the flaking was not up to original standards by a long shot. To start with, my flakes did not travel nearly far enough over the face, and my tool kit was not nearly versatile enough. Over the years, as I went to college, served in the army, and started a career mapping with the U.S. Geological Survey, I experimented with every way of making flakes I could think of. While I knew that there were other flintknappers, I didn't meet them until after my own style was well developed. I got better and better, but those early Indians were still a tough act to follow. Finally I met Dr. Dennis Stanford of the Smithsonian who showed me an excavated collection from a Cody complex spearpoint workshop. That was as good as getting a textbook on the subject—better really, because it forced me to organize and write down the lessons as they revealed themselves. Once the right door was opened, I found it a heck of a lot easier to gain on those ancient experts.

Who today wants to travel that laborious route to insight? "Not I" you say, and so we come to why this book exists. There are other books already, and I encourage you to read them, but this book is designed to let you appreciate something of how the original crafters of stone thought and felt about their job. Every new revelation is exciting and there is so much forgotten knowledge that it will take years to retrace the processes, even if we find a convenient shortcut or two.

## THE ROCKY ROAD TO NOW

The term "flintknapping" was coined to describe the manufacture of gunflints. Not all stones that can be worked into tools are flints, but somehow the label has stuck. Over the course of time, any activity of shaping brittle stone by breaking it has come to be known as knapping. To truly appreciate the working of stone, we should bear in mind that it was essentially a commercial venture. Knapping was not just a sideline, it ultimately stocked the larder and maintained a standard of living. Keep in mind that knapping was important to early people in every corner of the world. It doesn't belong exclusively to any culture.

We know that early, supposedly "primitive" people made and used stone tools routinely. Therefore, it comes as something of a shock that replicating tools should be so difficult. Why should that be?

Truth is, making stone tools did not come easily to mankind. Our ancestors had to interpret their experience with naturally sharp edges of rocks and then learn to manipulate the process. The greatest accomplishment was that they managed to convey their information to succeeding generations.

In order to understand flintknapping it is helpful to look back to its origins. From a handy, sharp protrusion of a rock, the concept of a handaxe in a sense shaped itself. Early man's experience showed that by striking one rock with another in a certain way, he could extend the available sharp edge into an even more useful tool. Beyond that, selective placement of the blows could ultimately result in the pear-shaped form we call a handaxe.

Clearly, stone tools first evolved in response to functional requirements. Designs that seem to strive for artistic values like symmetry show up only much later. It took hundreds of thousands of years for symmetry and thinning to gain full expression. First, people had to conceive what a tool could do before it could be improved. While we tend to view the early efforts at toolmaking as crude, they really represent an enormous step in abstract reasoning. Early stone tools had to be invented without benefit of prototypes or templates.

The stage was set. Suddenly (at least in a historical sense), raw stone was seen in terms of potential forms, and the variety of form brought with it a need for control over technique. No longer could just any hammer work, nor could the tool be used haphazardly.

The flaking technique that led the trend away from handaxes is known as "Levallois" (Le-val-wah). It was characterized by the careful trimming of the parent "core" of stone to predetermine the shape of the desired tool, prismatic for some tools, disc or turtlebacked for others. A final blow on such a prepared core would yield a flake that could be immediately put to use without further modification

With the discovery of such specialized flakes came new developments in striking tools. Craftsmen found that hammers of organic materials, such as antler, worked better on sharp edges because they absorbed some of the shock of the blow. People also found that edges could be strengthened and blunted by removing small flakes. Once edges were specially prepared in this way, heavy blows were easier to control.

Somewhere along the line, flintworkers got the idea that organizing successive blows allowed the same kinds of flakes to be created each time. Several types of cores were developed to avoid the considerable waste of stone that was associated with Levallois cores. By removing long, slender flakes, or blades from a conical core, many more tools could be created with the same effort. Such specialized flakes were used as-is, and the cores from which they were made were thrown away. This technique has been lauded for its efficiency in using as much of a stone as possible, but that really depends on how much was thrown away with the core and how long the flakes were kept in service as tools.

Core technology—where the flake is the objective, not the core—remained a dominant influence in European flintknapping up to the time that metal replaced stone. The fact that few places in the world have flint deposits that contain nodules suitably large enough for flake cores led to an alternative strategy that began with the handaxe form. This method of working on both faces is known as *bifacial* technique. Since flakes were discarded and only the core saved as a tool, it might appear to be a wasteful technique, but the tools were re-edged and

used again and again. In most of the New World, blades are rare and bifaces are dominant. The beautiful obsidian blades made by the Aztec Indians are perhaps the most notable exception.

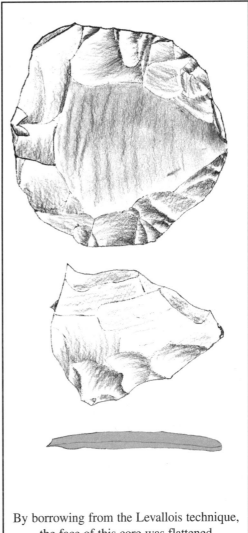

By borrowing from the Levallois technique, the face of this core was flattened dramatially with a single stroke. The flake is quite suitable for any number of tool forms.

The technology that this book describes applies mostly to the bifacial tools typical of the New World, although it does touch on several of the more significant elements of Old World core technologies. Specifically, the bulk of my background comes from evidence of Indians living on the high plains of North America. Keep in mind that some of my pronouncements may not fit as neatly to people that sprung from a different tradition.

I feel it is important to do more than just imitate the image of an artifact. My approach emphasizes total replication of ancient technologies, staying as close to the original methods, actions, and even thoughts as possible. Of course, we can never completely get into the mind of the aboriginal knapper, but let's see how close we *can* get.

Few places on earth have a continuous tradition of stone working that extends to our time. Australian aborigines still engage in stone tool making, as do some Mayan Indians. In Cypress and Turkey, people were lining the bottoms of threshing sledges with stone blades at least into the 1960's. The last Indian in North America to demonstrate completely traditional knapping techniques was Ishi, a Yahi Indian from the wilds of Northern California. From the time he entered the white man's world in 1911 until his death in 1916, anthropologists recorded as much of his culture as possible. Before that, only the occasional explorer had tried to describe the knapping process, and then with questionable degrees of success. The major problem they encountered was that flintknappers manipulate their tools in ways too subtle for an observer to easily pick out. A telling example is an early drawing published in 1919 by W. H. Holmes in the *Handbook of*

*Aboriginal American Antiquities. Part 1: Introductory and the Lithic Industries,* that attempted to clarify a photograph of an Indian knapping, taken by Hillers on the Powell expedition. The artist completely altered the position of the worker's hands. He drew what he thought should be going on, not what was actually happening. A further complication is that Powell was known for posing Indians to fit popular opinions of the day, although the position fits with good flintknapping practice today.

Modern efforts at flintknapping seem to have begun in Europe with the use of flint as a construction material. Buildings, faced with squared blocks of flint in the early 1300's, still stand in parts of Britain. When flintlock muskets came into vogue in the early 1600's, the industry was redirected into making flake-blades that scraped hot iron particles from the frizzle to ignite a gun's charge. During the Napoleonic Wars, the demand for gunflints established flintknaping as a substantial industry. Eventually, the continued need for gunflints led to the use of long blades of flint to achieve standardization as well as efficiency. A gunflint flaker in Brandon, Great Britain could tap out an average of 1,000 flakes a day from nearly a ton of flint, to help supply an export market of about 4,000,000 flints a year around the world.

As early as 1860, European knappers were beginning to turn their talents to recreating prehistoric weapons. William Smith and Edward "Flint Jack" Simpson were among the earliest replicators in Britain. Many kindred spirits have since joined in the quest to equal or surpass prehistoric craftsmen. Some are commercially driven, but an increasing number are more interested in the archaeological applications of artifact replication.

Smithsonian, National Anthropological Archives: 1609

Paiute Indian chipping a knife blade with a bone tool,

photo by John K. Hillers near Kanab, Utah 1872.

Holms' interpretation
(after Holmes,1919)

Patten's interpretation

Two artist's interpretation of the Paiute knapper's point of view,
contrasted with detail from previous page.  Note that the tool position drawn in 1919 is in
error by 90 degrees.

Today, when knappers get together, it isn't unusual to find that many of the techniques we came upon independently turn out to be strikingly similar. Other problems are solved in drastically different ways. Perhaps this recent pattern of development is an accelerated version of prehistoric development. I've tried to synthesize the wide experience of modern knappers as it best relates to the original masters of stone.

We have no way of knowing how long it took for aboriginal knappers to make their tools. Some ethnographic accounts relate the making of an arrowhead in fifteen minutes or less. Modern knappers can take from a few minutes to more than an hour, depending on how elaborate a point they are replicating or how familiar they are with the particular technology. Routine production of a particular kind of tool can easily become very efficient.

It is likely that just about everyone in earliest times knew the rudiments of knapping. After all, the use of stone was an everyday routine. Yet a few individuals must have shown special aptitudes for tool making, because every artifact style has its masterpieces as well as its clunkers. There is some archaeological evidence to suggest that there may have been specialists for separate tasks. One person might have hammered only the rough-outs, while another refined the preform by pressure flaking. The ultimate user of the tool might only have been responsible for its retouch and resharpening in the field.

A consequence of this kind of activity is that tools were seldom constructed from start to finish in one sitting. Preforms roughed out by percussion at the quarry might be carried some distance, with flakes removed as needed, for use as cutting tools.

Eventually, the remaining bifacial preform may have been used as a knife before finally being converted to a projectile point.

While men are generally presumed to have been the experts at knapping, women undoubtedly played an important role. Archaeological evidence from the R-6 Eden site in New Mexico has shown that even within the same culture, two distinct technologies may have existed side by side: one for hunting tools (presumably men), another for tools used within the camp (presumably women.)

The process of breaking a flake loose will not allow you to replicate artifacts if you do not have a clear idea of what the flake accomplishes Keep this notion in mind as you learn the basics and your learning curve will benefit. Each flake had a specific purpose, apart from making the core smaller. There is so much insight to be gained from the nuances of flakes that you will find an entire chapter devoted to the subject.

Every action of a knapper is reflected in his product and also in the castoff flakes, or debitage. This waste material forms an invaluable part of the archaeological record. Since stone survives long exposure to nature's chemistry better than anything else early man used, it provides a clear record of man's presence and actions. Even when the finished artifacts have been carted off, there is usually still enough evidence left in the debitage to tell what the knapper was up to.

## IS IT SAFE?

While debitage may be useful, it is also dangerous. A newly fractured edge is sharp and does not discriminate between cutting through animal hide or human flesh. The use of gloves or leather padding is advised for protection. After each blow, the loose pieces should be shaken away so they won't be driven into your skin at the next blow. Glass, whether man-made or volcanic (obsidian), is especially dangerous because it breaks into fine splinters. If there is a choice, practice on a less brittle stone such as flint or quartzite.

No matter how careful you are, chips are bound to fly into your face. Goggles are not exactly aboriginal equipment, but I suggest you wear them anyway if you value your eyesight. In the event a flake should get into your eye, do *not* try to rub or pick it out. Be sure to see a qualified eye special-ist immediately.

Cuts from a sharp stone edge may bleed a lot, but they usually heal quickly since the cells are not bruised. Have bandages handy. As in any situation, the best medi-cine is prevention, so try to keep sharp edges rasped off with a coarse-textured stone tool. Make sure you keep control of how your flakes fly off. Once a chip gains velocity, it can be very dangerous. Keep onlookers at bay so they will not be hit by flying flakes.

A less obvious hazard is the potential for silicosis. Breaking siliceous stone like flint fills the air with super- fine dust that cannot be thrown off by the lungs. Silica this fine can be absorbed by the bloodstream and recrystallized in the lungs. Enough of this kind of treatment and the lung tissue can be punctured from within. Knappers of gunflints in England were lucky to live to their mid-30's. Part of their problem was that they worked full time in a cramped shed full of dust. If you must work indoors, you should use a fine dust mask. Working in the open with adequate ventilation of clean air can also reduce the threat. Not much is known about silicosis, so it is wise to be especially cautious.

## A WORD ON ETHICS

Enough hardy souls have been active in flintknapping over the years that a serious question arises when the identity of a presumed artifact is challenged. How can we tell which artifacts are of recent manufacture and which are ancient? Unless some exotic material, like Brazilian agate or commercial glass is used, the answer may be that there is no reliable test. Replications should be indelibly marked or engraved with an identifying mark. Passing recent work off as old is unconscionable as well as illegal, but unfortunately it does happen.

Education in the analysis of artifacts is perhaps the best safeguard against misrepresentation. From a flintknapper's point of view, analysis is much more than shape and dimension. With proper training, it is possible to infer the tools used in the making of an artifact, how they were used, what modifications were made to the stone, and what sequence of events took place.

On that note, you should keep in mind that archaeologists have plenty to do without sorting through extra layers of evidence. Try to keep your knapping activities at home, or at least insure that your debris stays separate from site contexts. Most of my leavings go to the dump and some of it is buried with bottle-glass clues to its modern origin.

## WHAT KIND OF BOOK IS THIS?

When I started writing, I intended this to be a simple "how to" book. It still is but, in many ways it has also become a "how it was" book. In trying to figure out how to teach flintknapping to today's students, I've been plagued by the question of how prehistoric people communicated the same thing. Because of the gulf of time, I can only approximate the ancient methods of instruction.

As we have become "civilized," we have downplayed the linkage between psychology and physiology. When we set aside our intuitive perceptions, we lose much of our ability to take advantage of the many signals nature provides. A purely rational approach sometimes helps us do things that defy common sense, but it sometimes keeps us from considering "unscientific" ways of doing things. Our technical culture values mechanical explanations, while our ancestors were more content with accepting how the world works at face value.

It is likely that early men would have readily sensed energy transfers and force balances. The Zen approach of "being the stone" is not a bad substitute for engineering science. Flintknapping used to be as intuitive as seeing color. For some people whose tactile senses are well developed, it still is. However, most of us have to work hard to get a glimmer of what the early masters knew instinctively. Like a technician using electromagnetic patterns to define color, we use our mechanical knowledge of energy and force to define the way a stone will respond to the stroke of a hammer, even if we can't feel it.

My hope is that this book will help a reader to view flintknapping from a primal vantage point. As a primer, this book only describes first principles of flintknapping, with a strong emphasis on process. The challenge ahead of us is to decipher the remaining principles. Many people are taking an interest and are hard at work on the task. I think you will soon agree that our ancestors were potent problem solvers.

*Chapter 2*

# STONE

Flint is only one of many kinds of rock that can be flaked into tools. Each kind of rock has its own properties. We can describe properties of materials in detail not dreamed of in the past. We can also explore the earth as never before. We cannot, however, just go out and pick up whatever we want. Modern concepts of ownership block us from unlimited access to quality stone.

This chapter is intended as a general guide because I have no desire to set myself up as the guru of stone. You will learn what makes a stone workable, what kinds of stone meet these criteria, and how you can find some stone on your own.

## PROPERTIES

A stone's suitability for being knapped is controlled by just three factors: *structure*, *strength*, *elasticity*. Of these, only structure can be evaluated visually. Each piece of rock must be judged on its own merits. Whatever its chemical composition or scientific label, the qualities that control how a fracture can proceed are individual.

Even though the properties of stone are hard to evaluate directly, there are indirect measures that are easy to use. By simply taking a few sample flakes, you can learn the relative strength of stone. You don't need to know the number of pounds per inch the material will withstand. What you want to know is whether the stone breaks easily like glass or with difficulty like basalt. If you select your stone carefully for the right properties, it will make a huge difference in how well you can control the fractures you initiate.

A basic requirement for knapping is that the stone be uniform.  The big word is *homogeneous*, which means the structure is uniform.  It's okay to have grainy stone, as long as the grains are mostly the same size and are distributed evenly in the stone. An increase in grain size tends to make knapping more difficult but, as long as the grains are consistent in size and distribution, fractures can still be controlled.  Glass is not only homogenous, it is also fine-grained and has no visible structural features such as fibers, or layers to interfere with controlled fracture.

The bonding of individual particles within the stone is important to how strong a stone is.  If the cement bonding the grains together is as strong as the grains themselves, then a fracture is likely to travel smoothly.  If the bonding is weak, the fracture will take a tortuous path around individual grains. The strength of stone is not equivalent to hardness.  Some stones like jade, have a fibrous structure that bonds so tightly that a fracture cannot be controlled, if indeed it can even be started. While jade is too tough or tenacious to be flaked, it is soft enough that quartz can scratch it and it can be carved with relative ease.

Most homogeneous stones are also *isotropic*.  No matter which way the stone may be examined, the properties are the same.  Layers or zones of different composition within the same stone are serious obstacles.  As a break moves from one layer to another it tends to deflect much like light through a lens.  In crystal, fracture paths may change direction abruptly and regularly, like stair-steps.  Sometimes areas of crystallization exist within an otherwise uniform stone.  This causes localized irregularities of the fracture surface.

It is a lot easier to pull a stone in two than to squeeze it to pieces.  As we will see, knapping fractures can be controlled because they are in tension.  Some situations, like scraping, will be easier to deal with if the stone has a high tensile strength, but sometimes you want just the opposite.  There is no absolute value for tensile strength that can be said to be best.

Stop-action photos of the blade-making process show that blades bend as they are removed.  This ability to withstand bending and then return to the original state without damage is called *elasticity*.  If a stone lacks elasticity, then it is brittle and easy to break by accident.  The success of special effects like ribbon flaking relies heavily on the quality of elasticity to allow flakes to arc without breaking.  Elasticity is something you can feel, especially when flaking by pressure.  It is most obvious when a flake is slowly pressed off a glassy material.

Be a careful listener.  Much can be learned from the sound of a blow.  When a solid piece of good quality stone is struck, the whole stone vibrates at a frequency that produces a clear tone.  Flaws or cracks cause various portions of the rock to vibrate at different frequencies, which "muddies" the tone—a sound my wife terms "thuck" or "clack."  Since it is difficult to describe sounds, I suggest that the student simply pay close attention to the tones that result from using various tools on different preforms.

Many more clues as to how suitable the stone is for knapping can be found by examining a fractured surface.  The internal structure of the stone is best indicated by its texture.  Testing with a fingernail is a good way of checking for relative grain size by seeing how much the stone grabs it.  A hand lens may be used to see the texture

better and also check the shape of the grains. Angular grains lock together and rob some of the energy of fracture by friction. Surfaces that are highly reflective represent the finest structure. Matte surfaces usually indicate tougher stone. The presence of crystals or angular grains in the stone may be seen as a distinctive sparkle effect.

## TREATING STONE

It is sometimes possible to improve the flaking properties of stone through the use of heat. This method has been used for at least ten thousand years. How this change is actually brought about is still the subject of some controversy. My own experiments convince me that heating evenly distributes micro-fractures through the stone by expanding trapped moisture. Because of this, it requires less energy to initiate and control fractures. There is no hard and fast rule for determining which stone can be successfully heat-treated. When you make the stone easier to flake, you need to remember it is also weaker and can break easily in manufacture or use.

A slightly translucent stone is often a good sign, but the only sure test is to heat the stone and see if it's easier to work with afterward. Temperatures required to change the flaking properties range from 300 to 800 degrees Fahrenheit, depending on the stone. Too much heat expands the micro-fractures and causes internal crazing that, in essence, rips the stone apart. Rapid cooling does the same thing. To avoid this, it is advisable to cover the stone with dry sand to help even out temperature variations. It also helps to partially shape the stone ahead of time to lessen the mass through which the heat must be distributed. After treatment, the luster of the stone is improved and oxidation often lends it a red or yellow color.

A good method for modern experimenters is to use a slow cooker. All you need is 300°F (often the setting for high), and about 8 hours of cooking time. It is difficult to over-treat at this temperature and the long heating time minimizes damage. Not many stones will attain the super gloss that many modern knappers like, but the results will be close to most aboriginal treatments.

I would like to explain in detail how aboriginal knappers heat-treated their stone, but there are few archaeological indications of their methods. This suggests to me that the treatment may have been done in small batches, perhaps at the side of campfires. It may also be that the evidence has just been overlooked.

I am often told the story of Indians who heated stone and then got it to break as they wanted by dripping water on it. In spite of the usual force of conviction with which this tale is told, my experience is that it is a sure way to ruin good stone. The only evidence I know about for using water on hot stone is to start cracks in a massive

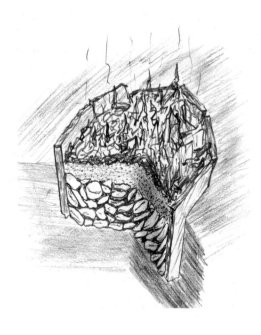

deposit of stone. This is a good time to wear your goggles, and other protective gear. After the crazed rock is cleared away, there may occasionally be small remnants that can be used. More importantly, you will find places to start prying big chunks out of the deposit.

Another means that has been proposed to make stone more workable is soaking it in water. Many instances have been cited where caches of flint preforms have been found in springs. If you ever get to mine flint, you can see that it is wet and relatively easy to break when it is fresh from the ground. As it dries, it becomes increasingly more difficult to knap. The neat thing about this approach to improving stone is that the finished tool retains its original strength.

## TYPES OF STONE

As I have said, the term *flint* doesn't apply to all the stones a knapper can work. Flint is a marine sedimentary deposit bound together by silica. A problem immediately arises in that other kinds of stones can be described in the same way, and experts argue over what is truly flint. A more generally applied term is chert. Usage of the terms *flint* and *chert* seems to be largely interchangeable, although finer-grained stones are often called flint while coarser ones are labeled chert. To add to the confusion, Europeans use the term *silex* in a way that seems to encompass both flint and chert. Leave the dispute to geologists and chemists; a knapper is more concerned with how a stone can be worked rather than with what it is called.

Pure, *crystal quartz* may be worked with much better control, but it presents other technical problems. Flaking in one direction may not reveal any difficulty because the fracture is compatible with the crystal structure. Trying to flake it the reverse direction, however, produces a stair-step fracture, and requires more energy. What we call quartz is the obviously crystalline occurrence of an oxide of silica. Aggregates of microscopic crystallization are given the various names of flint, chert, jasper, agate, chalcedony, opal, and so on. When the crystals are fine and evenly dispersed, then fracture is easy to achieve and control.

Chert, or flint, occurs most commonly as nodules in limestone or chalk. Ideally, the nodules will be flattened ovals of uniform quality. Nature has a way of promoting variety, however, and it is likely that the nodules will have holes and appendages. Most flint nodules are of best quality in the center, but you may find some that grade from prime quality at the outside to chalk in the middle. When the stone occurs as a solid layer, it is apt to be uniform throughout.

A lot of the silica in flint came from the organisms that built up on the seabed. is commonly formed as groundwater leaches away permeable parts of the rock and precipitates silica in its place. Both means of silicification can contribute to the same rock.

In the panhandle of Texas, a unique deposit of dolomite, similar to limestone, has turned into Alibates chert. Silica-rich ground water so gradually replaced the original deposits that the structure of the dolomite is still evident. Indians mined the deposit, then dispersed it over thousands of miles. The unique nature and colorful appearance of Alibates chert allows archaeologists to confidently identify its source wherever they see it. Alibates National Monument was created to protect the main portion of these quarries. Law prohibits collecting stone in the monument, but it is an interesting place to visit.

*Chalcedony* may look very much like , but it is formed by successive build-ups of silica instead of uniform replacement. Because of the mode of formation, chalcedony surfaces usually reveal smoothly rounded lumps. Agates are a special kind of chalcedony, characterized by translucent layers of different colors. Chalcedonies can be found in geologically active areas where silica-rich ground water has percolated through porous formations. Typically, chalcedony fills cracks and holes in surrounding rock. Sometimes, fossil material is slowly leached away and the resulting voids are replaced by silica. The outcome can be strikingly beautiful.

Chalcedonies whose iron content makes them appear red, brown, or yellow are usually called jasper. Jasper is known to occur in fairly massive deposits associated with igneous geologic features. In my experience, jasper is apt to have many fractures and crystal pockets, which tend to cause a great deal of waste. In many cases jasper has replaced wood and turned it into stone, or petrified wood. If the replacement is not thorough, the grain of the wood may still be evident when a fracture is attempted. This is one of the rare cases in which grain comes into play in knapping in the same sense as it does in carving.

*Opal* is a very light and brittle oxide of silica that has water chemically bound in it. It usually occurs as a result of opal secreting algae that live in hot springs or geysers and therefore is limited to concretions or as filled-in cracks and crevices of the parent rock formations. Exposure to the elements causes rapid decomposition of opal through drying out and thermal expansions and contractions. Precious opal is delicate, but knappable though the price may be prohibitive. Common opal comes in pastel colors and is easily worked if large enough pieces can be located. Clear, colorless opal is called hyalite.

An excellent source of knappable stone occurs where silica minerals have bonded together finely aggregated geologic deposits. If sand was the originally deposited material, the result is called *quartzite*. The quality of quartzite can vary tremendously, depending on the fineness of grain and the degree of silica bonding. The finest grain is called *siltstone* because silt is the primary building block. Quartzite is one of the most commonly used stones for knapping in the western U.S. Technical reports often refer to it as *orthoquartzite*.

In some areas, quartzite has a much different meaning. When great heat and pressure from mountain building have metamorphosed deposits of quartz, the resulting grainy rock looks like silicified sandstone. Unlike sandstone, however, bonding is much stronger. As a result, quartzite originating from metamorphism of quartz is a lot tougher to knap than sedimentary quartzite.

The processes of metamorphism create several other kinds of stone useful for knapping. Fine-grained rocks like shale and sandstone can work nicely when the bonding has been reinforced and homogenized by heat and pressure. If the alteration takes place on a large, regional scale, then metamorphosed shale is called *argellite*. A virtually identical-looking alteration caused by a local event, such as cooking along the flanks of a volcanic dike, is known as *hornfels*.

In Montana and Wyoming, there are places where exposed coal seams have caught fire and fused the surrounding shale into a solid, vitreous mass. Identified as *scoria* or *porcellanite*, this stone was much used by Indians. Now, it provides county maintenance crews with road surfacing material. If you can find the right roads, scoria can be easily picked up for knapping material without disturbing archaeologically valuable quarries.

*Meta-rhyolite* is a highly metamorphosed, igneous rock with definite bedding planes, found along the eastern seaboard. By taking advantage of the natural planes of weakness, it is easy to cleave large slabs as blanks. The difficulty with knapping meta-rhyolite is that there is a pronounced tendency for fractures to stop before they are completed. In spite of the difficulty of working meta-rhyolite, Indians could make a wide range of serviceable tools from it.

The next most available stone along the East Coast is *quartz*. Usually it is the variety known as bull quartz, which is white and full of random planes of weakness. A little more metamorphism causes the grains to be small and densely packed. As mentioned earlier, the highly metamorphosed variety of quartz is called quartzite. Artifacts of bull quartz or quartzite are chunky and crude looking, but they required considerable skill to make. Despite their ungainly appearance, such tools are just as usable as those made from better quality stone.

A major category of usable stones is volcanic in origin. *Obsidian* is the best known and most easily recognized of this group. The product of extreme fusion, obsidian is a natural glass with high silica content. Depending on the particular chemicals included in its formation, the color of obsidian can range through red, green, blue, or purple, but it will usually appear black. Inclusions sometimes render it coarse in texture and may weaken it. The main factor controlling the texture of obsidian is the rate at which the molten rock solidified. True obsidian simply cooled off too fast to crystallize. Rhyolite and granite were produced when cooling occurred more slowly. In fact, with age, obsidian slowly continues to crystallize or decompose by taking on water. The depth to which water has penetrated can be measured microscopically to estimate the length of time the surface has been exposed to the elements.

Slower rates of geologic cooling produce progressively larger grain sizes. The result is a family of rock types grading continuously from obsidian through rhyolite to granite. If no silica is present, the rock will be *basalt*. The gradations are subtle, and it may be difficult for a non-geologist to appreciate the distinctions. The fine structure of obsidian can be fractured with very low energy requirements. As grain size increases, greater force is required. This translates to stone being increasingly difficult to work. Gases present when the rock formed can cause air pockets that significantly interfere with controlled fracture.

The availability and ease of working obsidian causes many people to laud its virtues in knapping. However, obsidian also tends to splinter and this makes it a definite safety hazard. Once imbedded in the skin, a translucent splinter may be nearly impossible to locate. Special care must to be taken to dull sharp edges when working obsidian, as it is all too easy to drive an overlooked edge into your hand. Some of the slightly crystallized volcanic rocks, such as *ignimbrite*, or fine basalt, have nearly as good knapping qualities as obsidian, with far fewer safety drawbacks.

## WHERE TO FIND IT

It would be a monumental task to itemize all the sources of stone around the world. The next best thing is a short course in detective work. Road maps offer among the best clues. Place names like Flint Hill, Arrow Rock Creek, or Jasper Knoll quite often are a tip-off that a local source of stone may be available. Geologic maps are even more valuable, especially once an outcrop is spotted. It is an easy matter to check geological formations where they are accessible by roads or streams. The U.S. Geological Survey is a good source of both geologic and topographic maps of the United States in various scales.

Another effective way to scout for workable stone is to check gravel in the local drainage patterns. Once fragments of promising quality stone are noticed, it may only take backtracking upstream to find the source. Please, while in the heat of the search, do not forget to honor ownership rights. Many a fine quarry is now off limits because it was treated as public property. Ultimately, the best help may come from people who are the most familiar with the land. In some cases this means landowners, but there are also geologists, hunters, and rock hounds. If it is at all possible, look through local artifact collections and try to identify what stones were used by early knappers. That may at least provide a good idea of what there is to look for in your area, if not where to find it. Stone types which dominate collections are usually either the most available or the best quality around.

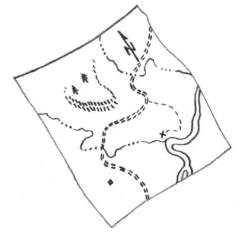

Modern construction is covering up a great deal of open land, but it also provides excellent access to geological structures. Sometimes excavation sites offer better quantity and quality of stone than an ancient knapper could have found. The source unearthed may not have been available in aboriginal times.

Rock shops may be of help in tracking down local stone for knapping. They can get rocks from other areas and will be willing to help on a commercial basis. Don't be afraid to spend a few dollars. One of the nice things about rock shops is that the stone they have available is often very attractive. Keep in mind that diamond saws and polishers give the lapidarist an ability to work with ease in stone that a knapper cannot even begin to manage. It pays to take along some good examples of the particular qualities you may have in mind.

Once you find a source of workable stone, there are some points of protocol to observe. Archaeologists see quarry sites as a valuable source of information. They have a fearsome enough puzzle to solve without having modern debris distort the evidence or worse yet, discover that evidence has been removed. Avoid archaeological sites and keep your workshop activities away from places that could interfere with archaeological interpretation. Some knappers go so far as to register their workshops with the local archaeological site registry.

The best thing a modern knapper can do at an ancient quarry site is to use it as a lesson book. The debris may not look like much, but experts left it. Generations of experience are represented and it is difficult to improve on such long tradition. Pay attention to what was discarded as well as what was favored. Early knappers were

efficient at grading out the best stone to work on. The effort needed to move and process stone makes a difference in how you pick and choose. Think of having to lug the stone from the quarry on your own back. Quality is important, but so are size, shape, and freedom from flaws. You don't have the same restrictions as the aboriginal knapper, but you should keep them in mind if you want to understand their work.

The use of the word *quarry* may be a little misleading if it is thought of in the modern context as prominent pits. Early man could only scratch out a small bit at a time with limited tools and only created really large excavations by generations of effort. Many aboriginal quarries are no more than an exposure of gravel on a hillside, recognizable only by an abundance of sampling flakes. If the stone occurs as an outcropping, more work is required. Thin ledges of stone are sometimes more desirable than the obvious thick ones. You don't waste as much or work as hard if you can find stone that is close to the right shape to begin with. Solid outcrops sometimes show evidence that fire and water were alternately used to loosen manageable chunks of stone. Where hot stone was splashed with water, you find discarded piles of highly fractured and discolored stone.

Aboriginal knappers seldom finished a product at the quarry. Usually the stone was shaped into forms designed for ease of transport as well as efficiency of further reduction. If a stone deposit lent itself to special treatment because of its shape or structure, you can bet the aboriginal miners figured it out and used it.

The importance of exactly identifying and describing a particular stone source comes into play when tracking movements

of prehistoric people.  In this context,
analysis can reveal the range of a group,
trading patterns, aesthetic preferences and
the physical constraints inherent in having
only certain stones available.

Flushwork created by setting shaped flint blocks in concrete.
Church at Long Melford in Great Britain.

The original of this Aztec knife design is set with a stunning mosaic of colored stone.

# Chapter 3

# TOOLS

A knapper has a lot to consider when selecting a tool. Do you want to hammer, punch, or press a flake off? What kind of support will you use? Are organic materials like bone or antler either suitable or available? Can you find the right kind of rock? Is metal a valid replacement for other tool materials? The bottom line is that the relation of a knappers tools to his style of working is special and unique because each person has to adapt to his own physique and goals.

You are apt to choose different tools than someone else, depending on available materials, what you want to replicate, and what cultural history you choose to follow.

Each tool can have many uses because, depending on how it is manipulated, it can yield a range of effects. While hammering or pressing are quite different actions, their range of results overlaps considerably, much to the chagrin of archaeologists who would like to determine tool use with greater certainty.

In the past, most tools were made of locally convenient materials and matched to the hardness of the stone being knapped. Metal tools were sometimes made from nuggets or meteors, but were not common before the Iron Age. Modern knappers often take advantage of a wider range of options for tool materials.

## HAMMERS

Common sense says you need something hard for a hammer, yet we also talk about "hard hammer" percussion and "soft hammer" percussion. The difference is in whether you want severe stress on the stone or not. Usually, stone hammers are considered hard hammers and are usually limited to primary reduction stages. Soft hammers made of antler or wood are called batons and are good for refining preforms. Besides hardness, hammers need to be durable, tough, and be able to "grab" the surface they hit.

The quickest way to see which rocks work best as stone hammers is to look at evidence from archaeological sites. Most of the hammers are rounded and tough. Toughness is what keeps the hammer from breaking apart after repeated blows. If the hammer is too solid, it can shatter your core. For example, a steel hammer often ruins good stone because stress builds up too quickly. Copper evens out the stress of impact, but I am aware of only a few archaeological examples where large nuggets were used as hammers. Greenstone, basalt, and quartzite all make good, hard hammerstones that are not too severe. Granite should never be used because the feldspar in it cleaves and the hammer goes to pieces.

Choosing the proper hardness of hammerstone requires both common sense and experience. Generally, the hardest stone hammers are used for quarrying, or to work tough stone. As more fragile stones are encountered, it is better to try softer hammers such as limestone or sandstone. After prolonged use, a hammerstone becomes pitted enough to soften the impact,

This hammer of greenstone is very tough and shows damage only on the ridges after years of use.

Made of hard, silicified sandstone, this tool serves double duty to strike flakes and grind preform edges. Note the grooves that develop after repeated grindings.

no matter how hard the hammer. When flaking a delicate stone, it may help to use a hammerstone that has been softened from use.

A hammer with a gritty surface grabs hold of the edge of the stone so glancing blows can be effective instead of skidding off. Silicified sandstone grinding stones were commonly converted to hammers for this reason. Used properly, gritty hammers can work as well as other tools for percussion. They also may double as abraders for grinding down an edge. The challenge is in finding a hammer with good grain, yet which is cemented together well enough that it does not fall apart with use.

Although stone hammers are serviceable through the whole range of percussion stages, organic materials are often considered superior, especially for later stages. The advantage is largely in their ability to transfer energy smoothly, but they are also strong and tough. The most commonly encountered organic percussor is antler. Normally, the antler is most dense where it attaches to the animal's skull. A cross-section of antler shows a spongy core, which carried blood, surrounded by a dense wall. Moose antler, which has a dense inner structure and very thick walls, is especially good for heavy percussion. Lighter tasks are best done with lighter kinds of antler, like deer or elk.

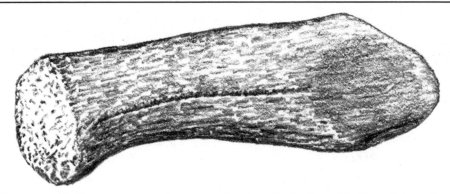

The extremely dense structure of moose antler gives the best combination of strength and weight. Only the largest stages of percussion need such a powerful tool.

Most percussion tasks can be done with this tool of deer antler. The contact end is the dense part that anchored into the skull.

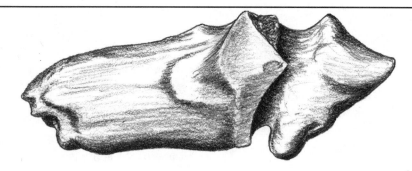

The heel bone of a buffalo is dense enough for percussion if it has not weathered first. Archaeological examples have been found with stone chips still imbedded.

Other organic materials can also be used. Ivory, with its almost solid structure, was a favored material for a percussor during the ice age. Today, it would be extravagant to use ivory for percussion. Certain types of bones are also strong enough for percussion use. The Indians of North America sometimes used bison heel bones, also called calcaneum, as percussors. The problem with bone is that it rapidly dries and gets brittle. Most knappers want tools that last.

Some knappers use dense wood for percussion tools. Wood evens the force of impact even more than antler. It should be considered when you know that shock would be apt to break the preform. The best woods to try include oak, mock orange, lilac, rhododendron, and tropical hardwoods. Since parts of the world don't have large, antlered animals, the ability to substitute wood would have been a real boon to primitive people.

## PUNCH TOOLS

On occasion, you want to combine the force of percussion with the precision of pressure by hitting an intermediate tool. A punch is a good solution when you don't have an accurate swing. Punches are also useful for getting at awkward places, like notches. The same materials that are suitable for percussion tools are good to use as punches. Splitting is a constant problem with bone or antler punches, so they tend to have ragged tips. Most punches are shaped as stout cylinders for strength. If the punch is used for notching, then it must be thin to reach into the work area without binding. A delicate punch takes a lot of shaping between hits to keep the tip square and solid. Some ancient people used copper or soft iron for punches and some modern

Beaten copper is strong enough to make deep, narrow notches.

knappers do the same thing. Metal provides more than strength; it can be chosen for just the right give and will be consistent each time it is used.

## PRESSURE TOOLS

Unlike hammerstones and punches, pressure tools don't depend on velocity or mass to break the rock. Instead, they simply need to be strong enough that the knapper can break off flakes by muscle power without buckling the tool. Contrary to what you might think, the tool doesn't have to be very hard. In fact, it is important that the antler be just soft enough to let the stone edge dig in slightly. It will then act to lever a flake loose from the surface of the stone. Not all antlers are satisfactory as tools. Old antlers may be soft from weathering, or lack minerals. Good antler is usually fresh and solid.

A whole antler tine provides amazing stiffness and strength. It is difficult to hold the curved, tapered tine without slipping, so you might wrap it with some leather to make the grip more comfortable.

A spline cut from the antler wall is more flexible than an entire tine. The extra spring can be a real help in pulling flakes loose. I like to cut pressers from the walls of old antler batons. They can be sharpened to pointed sturdy tips and I'm not always looking for new tines. Eskimos perfected a specialized handle to mount splines of various materials as presser tips. The handle is designed to fit comfortably in the palm of the hand. Tips of antler, ivory, bone, and even copper were scarce and used sparingly in a land of ice.

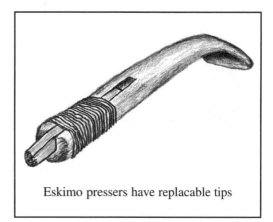

Eskimo pressers have replacable tips

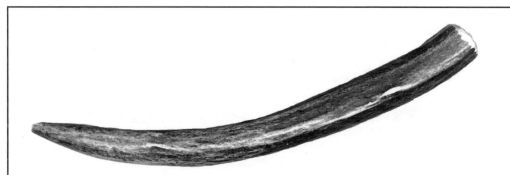

Mule deer tines are straighter than those of white-tailed deer, but both otherwise serve equally well. The tips need to be smoothed off to avoid splintering. Too much wear reveals a soft interior.

One can obtain extra leverage by tying the presser to the end of a long stick. Ishi, the last Indian in North America to grow up free of White influence, used such a devise. It is often called an Ishi stick in his memory. Another way to extend the power of pressure is to use an Ishi stick fitted with a crosspiece, like a crutch. South American Indians were very adept at using chest crutches to obtain long obsidian blades. On occasion, a projection on the crutch would be struck like a punch to aid detachment of the blade.

Bone and ivory are common and effective alternatives for antler pressers. Australian aborigines have been observed using their own teeth for flaking, but it is only good for light retouch and your dentist might disapprove.

Modern knappers often use copper for pressure flaking. Examples have been found of Indian making flakers from nuggets of native copper. It isn't evident that any culture used copper more than other kinds of flaking tools. Danish dagger handles, for example, have a peculiar kind of flaking that seems to be most easily and accurately duplicated by using copper tools, but the rest of the work could be accounted for by antler tools. To my knowledge, there is no foolproof means of distinguishing between work done by copper and antler tools.

The shape of the tool tip can strongly influence the effects that can be obtained. On the other hand, I often do detailed work with a stubby antler tip while other knappers insist on a sharp point to make the same kind of flake. It is good to avoid preconceptions of what works and what does not.

Some tools need notches for hafting or to make a serrate edge. A spatulate tool can be narrow and strong enough to get into small openings. Specialized notching techniques, discussed in chapter 7, call for cone shaped tools for pressure notching or toothed spatula tips for mini-percussion. Copper works for notching because it is strong and is easy to keep in shape. Copper becomes work hardened, so it is best to shape a tip by pounding rather than by filing it. A rod of copper may be mounted in a handle to keep it from bending and to hold it easily. If you feel that the copper is too hard, all you have to do to soften it is to heat it.

Pressure tools can be made of soft metal although only small amounts of meteoric iron or native copper were available in early times.

## SUPPORTS

While you can use your own flesh and bone to support cores and preforms while they are being worked, you are apt to complain about the wear and tear. The most standard support is a leather pad to protect the knapper's hand from chips and impact of the tool. It helps to have a thick, flexible piece of leather. Buffalo hide is good because it has interlacing fibers that resist wear and tear. Rawhide may be used, but it needs to be limbered up first by bending or pounding. My personal preference is to work the leather to a chamois-like softness. It allows me to nest the preform on edge so the presser isn't trapped against my hand.

Some special pressure flaking effects (described in chapter 7) may require block supports built of wood, hard leather, or rubber. Flat flake scars typical of Eden style artifacts can be created by using a supporting block to incline the preform edge. Some people are simply uncomfortable with holding preforms in their hand and prefer to work with blocks and wedges.

A few knappers have found that a forked stick can serve as a block by resting the preform on top of the fork and levering the flaking tool through the saddle of the fork. Similar effects can be obtained by manipulating the hand to leave a gap under the preform, but the hand is not a stable support and results may be erratic.

Vises help to control where flakes travel by immobilizing cores or preforms. There is no archaeological evidence confirming that vises were used for stonework, although their use has been suggested to explain blade cores and shearing off the faces of some projectile points. A simple vise can be constructed by loosely tying the halves of a split branch near the end to be used as a pincers and then driving a wedge between the halves at the other end. You can make another type of simple vise by lashing together the ends of a narrowly forked branch.

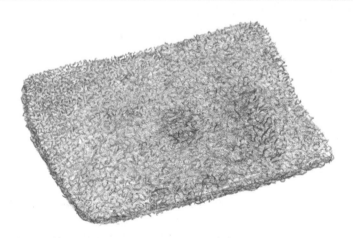

A thick pad of buffalo rawhide is an effective protection for the knappers palm. Long, interlaced fibers resist wear and retain stiffness through the making of many artifacts.

Sometimes thin or fragile stones need stiffeners of wood, bone, antler, or leather applied as backing. In some cases, it may be necessary to glue them in place with resin.

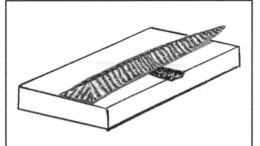

A chipping block helps to keep the flake scars in a plane for special effects.

Cores or preforms can be steadied by a vise made from a split limb by tying one end and wedging at the other.

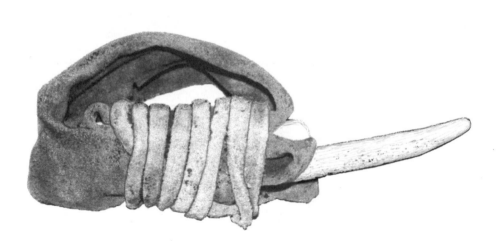

While this tool is not known from direct archaeological evidence, it is invaluable for making long, ribbon-flake scars consistent with some of the finest paleo-period knapping. The grip comfortably increases the force directed forward at the tool tip, made from a section of elk antler. The same tool enhances Eden style flaking by applying consistent pressure to take each flake off as a small blade.

## GUNFLINT TOOL KIT

When Brandon, Suffolk in England was the center of the gunflint industry, the workers used a specialized set of tools that made standardization possible. In spite of the wide distribution of gunflints, knappers were paid only a pittance for their effort. Tools were simple and handmade to keep costs down.

Short-handled hammers were used to break nodules cleanly in two. These quartering hammers were made of soft railway iron and weighed 3 to 3 1/2 pounds. Knappers then used lighter, short-handled hammers to strike long blades off the quartered sections of stone. The flaking hammers used to make blades were symmetrically squared and pointed to about 1/8-inch at the tip.

Knapping hammers to section the blades were made of files broken to 4-inch lengths. The ends were squared and thinned to under 1/6-inch at the tip. Flint blades were snapped and shaped into flat, square gunflints on top of a 3-inch high, flat-headed iron stake driven into a stump. A staging pad of leather at the base of the stake causes the hammer to rebound for the next stroke.

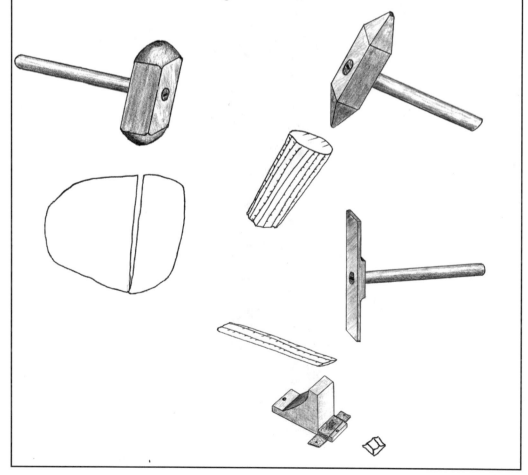

*Chapter 4*

# BREAKING ROCK

Before you take up tools and start knapping, you should get acquainted with why and how stone breaks. This chapter addresses the role of energy, with little concern for direction because energy is only potential until it is spent. In the following chapter you find out how force consumes energy along directed paths.

One of the biggest problems a beginning flintknapper faces is finding a detailed description of the knapping process. Even seasoned veterans acknowledge that the state of the art is far from complete. Only a few, limited conditions can be described by mathematical equations. Extending those results to more general knapping practices is like predicting the weather—you may be right, but was it because of the formula? The usual approach in archaeology has been to measure characteristics thought to be important, and try to find significant correlation. Even when attributes are related, the reasons often remain obscure.

Since precision doesn't help a layman understand how to break rock, we can shift to looking at more general qualities to understand how knapping works. In this chapter, we will explore the idea that there is a tidy relationship between how much energy is supplied to the stone and how it is used up when the stone breaks. An energy balance can be easily dealt with on an intuitive basis, as we will see. For those with a more technical bent, the energy balance has the potential to be studied with all the scientific rigor of modern civilization.

In its simplest form, the energy balance says that the energy applied is exactly offset by the amount of energy dissipated. This is no more than the conservation of energy law. Once you know the factors on each side of the equation the trick is to do the things that work toward controlled fracture. If special effects, such as overshots lose energy, then you need extra energy to compensate. Applied energy should be viewed as capacity to do work, and dissipated energy as work done. Energy is described mathematically as $MV^2/2$, where M is mass and V is velocity. It isn't important to know the values in this expression, but it is critical to get a feel for what factors can be influenced to control the energy. This equation makes it clear that energy can be increased by a corresponding increase in either mass or velocity. In simple terms, to get more energy with which to do the work of knapping, use a heavier hammer or swing faster.

A peculiar thing about energy is that it doesn't care a bit about direction. Don't worry for now about angles between the knapping tool and the core. There will be plenty of that in the next chapter.

According to the law of conservation of energy, energy can be transferred from one place (or object) to another by doing work. In addition to the energy from the weight and speed of the baton, muscles in the knapper's arm can add more energy. The rate at which force is imparted is known as power. In other words, a powerful blow provides a great deal of energy to be used up in fracture. It is important to keep power in mind as a source of energy distinct from the weight and speed of a baton. In the case of pressure flaking, it is certainly the dominant source of energy.

**Factors of applied energy**

Mass (weight)
Velocity (speed)
Power (muscle)

## EXPENDING ENERGY

There are a lot more ways to use energy than to supply it and they are difficult to describe. While we would prefer all the available energy to go into a controlled fracture, it isn't likely to happen in a hand-operated system. A list of potential factors of energy loss illustrates the complexity of the problem:

**Factors of energy loss**

Controlled fracture
Shatter
Bending
Compression
Rebound
Movement
Material flaws
Tool damage
Time
Platforms
Size
Support
Arm tension
Water

The concept of energy balance is most obvious for percussion. Pressure methods of flintknapping follow the same rules except that more energy is spent to support your work and the direction that force is applied becomes more important.

### Controlled fracture

The goal is to get rid of things that keep a fracture from going as you want it. When the factors that tend to rob energy from the primary goal are controlled, then the fracture will go right. It might seem fruitless to devote so much discussion to the things we don't want to happen. Hang in there, the reward is a control of fracture that is astonishing.

### Shatter

One of the most notorious energy robbers is shatter. When this happens, lots of fractures occur. It just doesn't contribute to shaping a tool. A major culprit in causing shatter is a fragile edge. When a knife-edge of brittle stone is hit, no matter how carefully, it tends to collapse. The blow forces fragments against the preform causing yet more lines of fracture. Even if the impact site is stable, shatter can still occur from too fast a blow or too hard a tool. Flaws buried within a stone can cause shatter in spite of anything else you may do. See the section on material flaws for hints on how to anticipate flaws.

In the jargon of the flintknapper, the impact site, where you hit the stone, is referred to as a platform. Preparing a stable platform is one of the most crucial skills a knapper can develop. Details of platform preparation are treated in chapters 6 and 7, but there are several general options are available to reduce shatter. The simplest approach is to select an area along the edge that is at a steep angle to the face you want to flake from. If there is no such place to hit, you can bevel the edge back steeply using either pressure or percussion methods. Either of these choices can still allow shatter from a hard blow, so it is often

necessary to round the edge with an abrasive like sandstone or quartzite. The amount of grinding that should be done will depend on the speed and hardness of the hammer.

It is important to keep in mind that shatter is more likely with dense, unyielding hammers. Soft hammers diffuse the energy gently over an area and rarely cause shatter when even the most elementary platform preparation has taken place.

Pressure flaking is not immune to the problems of shatter either. The same rules apply with a reduction in scale because the forces involved are applied more gently.

## Bending

Bending causes some of the most irritating damage a flintknapper experiences, like snapping flakes off short or breaking the preform in two. Bending happens when the hammer force doesn't line up with forces from the support. The result is that one side of the preform is in compression and the other in tension. Since stones are so weak in tension, it does not take a very hard blow to cause enough bending to break a preform. It is especially common for bend-related breaks to happen when the blows are near the end of a preform. This phenomenon is known as end-shock and the breaks commonly occur across the center of a preform.

Use common sense to reduce bending. One way is to just rest the core lightly on the fingers while striking off a flake. For larger pieces, it may be necessary to rest the preform along your leg while lightly elevating the working edge. These methods of minimal support allow very thin bifaces to be made with small chance of breakage because there are not enough external forces to bend the preform.

Paradoxically, bending can sometimes be countered by locally extreme support. When flakes are breaking off short due to bending of the flake, it pays to try pinching the preform close to the striking platform. This keeps the force parallel to the face of the stone and allows the flake to shear off the face.

When bending is avoided, flakes tend to come off straight. Sometimes you want curved flakes but you have to be careful that the bending is only enough to arc the flakes and not so much that it breaks the preform. Often, it is desirable to slightly rotate the preform against the blow, to cause the flake to arc along the surface. One of the benefits of this technique is that bad spots can be reached from the far edge when all else fails. This stategy was favored by many early knappers and is recognized by the archaeological terms of outrepassé, or overshot flakes. Modern knappers often complain about these effects, but that is just because they do not understand how to control them.

While doing pressure work, it is particularly important to keep bending in mind because there are so many forces at work. Under certain conditions overshots can be a significant problem. Many times you want the flake to arc across the top of the preform, but if there is any pressure on the far edge it creates bending that makes the flake cut through to the opposite face, taking off a chunk of the far edge. When that happens, there is no choice but to make a narrower product. The other major bending related problem develops when the points of support are too far on either side of the applied force. It is like a bridge that collapses in the middle because the span is too wide. That is why we call it bridging. Tension develops on the face opposite impact and the piece is apt to snap in two unless it is uniformly supported or fairly thick.

## Compression

Compression is another way to use up energy. In most circumstances, this effect goes unnoticed because contrary to bending, compression strengthens the stone. Back to the bridge analogy, failure is mostly in the tension cables, not in the supporting columns. Compression exists every time the preform is struck. When a long flake is taken, the flake is in compression for the duration of the fracture. Because stones are more stable in compression than in tension, the flake is strengthened while force is transferred down its length. If the direction of force pulls out of alignment with the fracture, compression is lost and the flake can break off short. This is known as step fracturing, or stacking of flakes when a series of step breaks occur. When compression is too great, it contributes to bending and the formation of overshot flakes.

## Rebound

When it is hit, stone wants to go back to its original shape and, if it doesn't break, it bounces. You can't see the stone bend or compress but it happens, like pool balls bouncing off each other. When energy is lost, it may be after a fracture has started to penetrate. That becomes a buried flaw that interferes with any other attempts at flaking through the same area. A potential problem

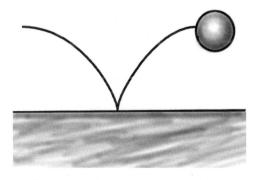

with rebound is that a second impact can start more than one fracture. If the knapper chooses to be generous with the energy loss and hit harder than necessary, the hammer should be pulled back after the first contact to avoid chatter. It is more appropriate to minimize bounce by increasing speed or power.

## Movement

If the core is just too solid for a fracture to start, the energy will move the core rather than break it. This may be what you wanted, but at least it lets you correct the problem and try again. When the core is supported so well it cannot move, a bad blow can really cause lots of damage. Even when the fracture takes place as planned, movement of the core helps to use up extra energy if the blow is too hard. One way of supporting a preform to allow movement is to cradle it loosely in an envelope of leather. Extremely thin bifaces can be made this way without much chance of damage because, by allowing the core to move, you avoid bending and possibly breaking it.

## Material flaws

A flaw, whether it is in the stone or in the hammer is an insidious robber of energy. The force of the blow is dissipated and vibrations can generate fracture from the inside out. Flaws in the stone can be crystal pockets, inclusions or hidden cracks. You can sometimes find flaws because a stone gives a dull, clunking sound when the stone is tapped. Hitting the preform without regard for buried flaws often allows energy to expand the flaw into a crack that can split your preform. If the flaw is a crack, it can sometimes be developed, and thereby disposed of, by a steady tapping on the stone. If the tone of each tap rises, it reveals when the crack is extending. You may be able to work around or even through a crack or flaw, but its better to sacrifice some material by getting rid of the problem rather than have the work literally go to pieces.

### Tool damage

Repeated blows on a sharp edge cause the hammer or presser to get mushy and rob energy. Tool ends should be ground smooth periodically so that they transfer energy efficiently. It is quite possible for the stone to dig into a soft spot on the tool and take a big bite out of the tool edge. Stone hammers are often self-renewing in the sense that as parts slough off there is still solid material underneath. But, if the cement that holds a hammer together crumbles, it can damage the edge of the preform. If the knapper notices a deadening of the sound or feel of his blows, the damaged hammer should be repaired or thrown away before it breaks. Tool damage can be useful to soften a hammer enough that it doesn't shatter the fragile edge of a brittle stone like obsidian.

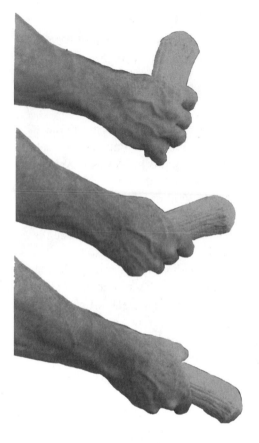

### Time

Fractures don't happen all at once. The progress is incremental, with the detached portion of the flake acting something like a lever to transfer force to the fracture front. When a blow is delivered faster than the stone can break, the fracture surface ripples. Not only is control of that flake lost, but the next flake is will have trouble getting past the roughness. The smoothest surfaces can occur when energy is delivered slowly and steadily. A slow swing goes against a knapper's natural inclination, but gives good results. It's best to tighten up on the hammer to add power, because low speed by itself means low energy. This technique is seldom used by modern knappers and appears to have been used often by ancient flint workers.

### Platforms (impact site)

Platforms are more a factor of efficiency of energy transfer than energy loss. An improperly constructed platform allows energy to be lost by shatter or movement. A platform must be a stable impact site. It is easy to be overzealous and make a platform too strong, so try for just strong enough. When a hammer hits a platform, the area over which the impact is spread controls the pressure that comes to bear. A small platform causes more load and allows the flake to release much more easily than a large one. There are trade-offs that make the choice less simple than it appears. If the stone is especially tough, it may need careful platform isolation to allow the flake to get started. A platform that is too small to carry the energy required for a fracture will collapse. Each situation must be evaluated in its own light but, with experience, a knapper will know what kind of platform is needed.

Special treatment of platforms can make it easier to start flakes. It is well known that abrading the tops of obsidian cores makes it easier for the blades to release. Creating micro-fractures at the surface allows a fracture to begin at a lower energy level than an unblemished surface would allow. The same thing happens when a platform edge is abraded. On a larger scale, big bifaces can be battered along the edge to drive in cracks, and then ground to round the edge. In spite of the grinding, incipient cracks remain that allow flakes to start readily. The ease of taking large flakes in this manner will surprise you.

Platforms need to be matched to the tool. You can take a flake with an antler tool against a pointed platform even though it might damage the hammer. A stone tool will shatter the same platform. Too solid a platform can make the fracture go deep and ruin the effect you are after. Accurately determining the right stability of a platform takes practice. Pay attention to what works.

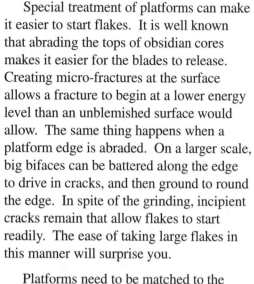

### Size

Matching the hammer size to the size of the core transfers energy effectively. A small hammer cannot even move a core without the aid of speed or power, much less remove a useful flake. You want enough weight in the hammer to allow the fracture to occur without needing speed or muscle, but not so much that it overpowers the preform.

At times, it may not be desirable or even possible to use a large enough baton. In these cases, muscle can be used to force the fracture to behave as if the size rule were being obeyed. One's natural inclination when using power is to brace against the blow, but that causes problems. Energy is lost through support, and bending is nearly unavoidable. A very loose support channels energy efficiently into a flat, controlled break. This technique works best with a short stroke to limit speed. The combination of too much speed and muscle seems to cause stresses too violent to control.

### Support

Many of the preceding sections have dealt with the role of the support, but it is worth looking at separately to be sure that we understand it. Support can be your grip on the tool or core, or it can be anything else that braces the core against movement. It is a factor that cannot be reduced entirely because a knapper has to hold the stone and not just toss the preform into the air like one would serve a tennis ball. You may think that only the force you apply has any effect, but physics assures that the support gets to push back.

The force imparted by the support generally needs to be either very small or crisp. What I mean by crisp is that it is undesirable to allow the support to give so much that it robs energy. This is a quality that is more easily felt than described. As an example, try a blow with the core resting on the fleshy part of the leg, and then compare that to the blow on a core resting on a rock. A solid support makes the core act as if it has more mass, but if it is too solid you may feel like you are hitting the anvil.

Vises are the ultimate support, and can be quite simply constructed. Two sticks lashed in the middle make a neat pincers vise at the one end if a cobble is wedged between them at the other end. Other aids like sticks or pads of leather can be used to help insure that no portion of a preform is subjected to bending. When very long preforms are being worked, it becomes a challenge to find combinations of arms, legs, and hands to brace the piece adequately.

Although immobilizing the preform completely uses considerably more energy than loose support, it allows some useful effects. When flakes are struck from an immobilized preform, they can shear virtually edge to edge. This technique takes a high degree of skill, but also can yield very clean, regular flake scars. Once the face has been flattened, I recommend a change from extreme restraint to very slight support.

With practice, a preform can be held on outstretched fingers so that almost no resistance is encountered. Even if you drop it, you will break fewer preforms than if you hold tight. An easier way to lessen support is to use a loose leather wad under the preform and then pinch the preform at the center of its faces. This way, if the blow is too hard or not aligned, the preform will pivot or slide out of the way and not be ruined.

## Arm tension

Arm tension is one of the toughest variables to control. Besides, using too much muscle wastes energy. Listen to the difference in sound between a hit with tension in your arm and without. The clearest tone (without tension) reveals the best transfer of energy. With practice, you can hold the hammer with a tight grip and still swing freely from the elbow. This makes the hammer work as if it shared the weight of your forearm. A tight grip combined with a loose swing is a key to being able to duplicate European blade technology. On the other hand, tension in your elbow can be tough on your body.

When you grip tightly, you increase other factors of energy loss, like bending and arm tension. A lot of energy is being applied and only a thorough understanding of how it is being used up keeps the knapper from damaging the work. If all factors are in balance, this technique is the most efficient one I know of for quick reduction of a preform.

## Water

When you looked at the list of energy loss factors, you may have wondered why water was included. Recent studies have shown that fracture of silica based materials is extremely sensitive to the presence of water. Especially when stress is present, water molecules get into a crack and chemically attack the bond between silica molecules. The effect can lower the energy required for initiation of fracture by as much as 20 times and speed the advance of a crack up to a million times. Cracks have been observed to advance at speeds up to 1,100 meters per second, although you will not be working in this range.

Oddly enough, the role of water in promoting crack formation has the potential of explaining how stones can be treated both by soaking and by heating. Soaking porous rocks increases the water that is available at the leading tip of the crack, as long as the stone can be kept damp. Heating causes stress through differential expansion that magnifies weaknesses in the stone when water, already in the rock, attacks silica bonds. Instances are known of steaming flint to improve its workability. Presumably this would work two ways, first by introducing micro-fractures and then by providing enough water in the body of the stone to make knapping easier. Numerous caches of preforms found in springs show that early people recognized the value in keeping stone wet.

## IT DOESN'T HAVE TO BE COMPLI-CATED

It requires practice to develop manual dexterity. Flintknapping is no different, although it is so complex that it may take years to reach the highest levels of proficiency. Muscle responses have to be programmed in so that the body reacts intuitively. Remember that the fracture is moving so fast you cannot react if something goes wrong.

We need to start with the variables that are easy to control. Platforms require some skill to make but are among the most important things a beginning knapper has to understand. Before you start knapping, choose tools of the proper size, and see that they are free of damage. As the work progresses, platforms may be adjusted to match the knapper's needs.

When it is time to apply the tool, the knapper has to predetermine all the active variable requirements. Speed, power, support, time, and movement all have to be coordinated for the fracture to go as planned. Use the loosest support possible and try not to force the blow. The only critical variable left is speed. This is easy to control by using a relaxed, easy swing and adjusting speed by lengthening or shortening the stroke.

Get proficient in the least complicated operations before mastering something like overshot flakes. Most archaeological evidence shows percussion being used at the simplest level anyway. Another important thing to keep in mind is that each ancient knapper worked within a specific cultural framework and had only a limited repertoire of techniques. Most modern knappers aspire to be proficient in several knapping traditions. This is somewhat akin to an artist mastering several painting styles. It isn't easy, but rate your self accomplished when you get there.

Now that we know how to provide the energy for fracture, the next chapter will show you how to make the fracture travel where you want it.

*Chapter 5*

# DIRECTING THE FRACTURE

It is not enough simply to get stone to break. The next lessons are designed to make the fracture travel just where we want it to go. The balance of forces acting on the flake as it develops influences the path the fracture will take. One component of force causes the break to extend, while another causes it to change direction. By combining forces judiciously, the knapper can select from a whole range of options to make the fracture travel where he wants. For the archaeologist, the results can reveal what the knapper did.

The balance of energy concept is most useful when the fracture happens fast. Most percussion fits this category. Slower acting techniques, like pressure flaking, involve a much different, but no less important kind of control.

In the last chapter, energy was discussed independent of direction. Now we want to talk about force as a way to move things in a particular direction. It is crucial to realize that a fracture doesn't happen in an instant. No matter how great the knapper's speed or power, the fracture starts from an edge and progresses molecule by molecule until the energy is used up. The action is too fast to watch, but still the fracture can be controlled.

Before tool is applied to stone, the flake is just a wish in the knapper's mind. As soon as the tool is applied, however, critical stresses cause a fine crack to begin around the area of contact. Considering the progress of fracture in small increments allows us to envision a series of progressively longer columns of stone separated from the core.

As we shall see, there is a direct relationship between the direction in which the force acts and the direction that the fracture takes. This becomes tricky when we try to resolve a complex array of forces into a distinct direction. It is easiest to understand what is happening by considering the simplest cases before moving on to the more complicated ones.

## WHICH WAY DID IT GO?

Let's imagine a very special, slender tool, which can only work in the direction the tool is pointing. Also imagine that no other force comes into play. When this magic tool is pressed against an edge, the break always extends where the tool is pointing. Pointing the tool along a face makes the longest flakes, while only short flakes can come from pressing perpendicular to the edge.

Of course, the real world doesn't work so neatly. A tool almost never exerts force exactly in line with its axis, and other

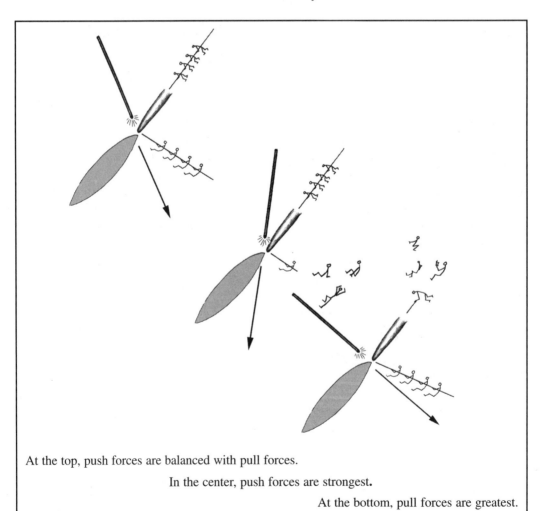

At the top, push forces are balanced with pull forces.

In the center, push forces are strongest.

At the bottom, pull forces are greatest.

forces are always present. In spite of this, it helps to keep a mental picture of the effective force as being some combination of two hypothetical forces. Flaking where force is directed along the axis of the flake is "push flaking." Conversely, when force is directed away from the preform, it can be termed "pull flaking" because the flake is being pulled away from the preform. Some authors define the components as inward and outward forces.

My experience with beginning knappers is that they can quickly grasp the idea of push and pull force components but still fail to apply it correctly. Although they start with a push force, they then tilt the tool perpendicular to the edge to establish the pull component of force. When the position of the tool is changed, the push force is reduced and all that is left is the pull force. What the knapper has to realize is that the direction the tool is pointing is not as important as the direction it is being shoved. Envision the magic tool as representing the effective combination of force. First push in the direction that you want a fracture, and then pull away to get the fracture started while making sure that you haven't stopped pushing.

Because force has to be transferred through the flake as it develops, the forces that start the fracture can never be the same as the forces along the leading edge of the progressing crack. In effect, the flake becomes a tool for its own creation. For a short distance, the formation of the flake is stable. After a while, though, it gets so thin in proportion to its length that its bending effects a change in the direction the force is acting.

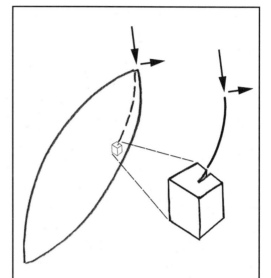

The knapping tool can only act directly on the edge of the stone. Forces at the fracture front are transferred by leverage action through the portion of the flake that has already detached.

No matter how brittle stone is, it still can yield and rebound within the limits of its strength. This elasticity makes it possible for our flake column to bend and steer force at the crack front in a different direction than the tool applies it. It is much easier to pull brittle stone apart by tension than to squeeze it to pieces in compression. For this reason, the column is strongest when forces are directed down its axis. Any other direction introduces tension on the outside of the bend. While the inside of the bend is in compression, that does not keep the column from breaking. If the tension exceeds the strength of the stone, only an external counter-balancing force, like light support on the face, can keep it together.

A long flake can only occur when forces are balanced throughout its length. Since both the stone and knapping tool can move, planning and coordination are important if one is to control the flake trajectory. Straightest flakes are those in which force is applied in perfect alignment. For example, in percussion, a vertical blow against a core resting on an anvil (your leg is a soft anvil) can make straight flakes. To make strongly curved flakes, the direction of force has to change even as the fracture progresses.

Curved flakes are best controlled in percussion if one coordinates the movement of the core with the movement of the tool. For example, Clovis-style flaking is accomplished by rocking the preform edge slightly upward while the baton arcs down. The result is a nice balance of force along an even arc. Few technologies show deliberate use of curved percussion flakes because it demands such a high skill level.

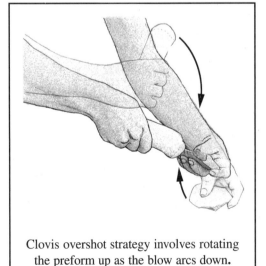

Clovis overshot strategy involves rotating the preform up as the blow arcs down.

## THE PRESSURE IS ON

Pressure flaking techniques offer many ways to make use of the flake as its own lever. Applying force slowly greatly increases the control that can be exercised over direction of fracture. The way you support the preform and grip the tool can contribute even more. Masters at pressure flaking rock the preform against the oncoming tool to extend slender flakes all the way to the opposite edge.

The simplest kind of pressure flaking is to lay the preform on a flat surface and press chips off the edge. Either push or pull flaking can be used in this way with virtually the same results. The flakes are too straight and short to do much more than make the edge neat. This style of flaking is used mostly for edge dressing on camp tools, or in preparation for another technique.

Tipping the preform on edge makes longer flakes possible, but they will not arc much as long as the support is rigid. If you want to do Eden-style flaking, use a wedge to hold the preform steady at a consistent angle. A flexible support, such as the palm of the hand, allows forces to act in an arc across the face of the preform. Parallel flaking is usually accomplished this way. The length of the flake is longest when the preform rocks most freely. Some knappers maintain the length of flake through a leather or rubber support, which serves to balance the force as the flake arcs.

As soon as longer flakes are taken, the differences between push and pull flaking styles start to become apparent. Push flakes can extend far without widening, and tend to feather out because forces stay aligned. Pulling flakes off distributes the remaining components of force radially in the plane of the flake. Thus, pull flakes are broader and tend to break abruptly when the flake gets too thin to support tension of the strong outward force. Refer to the illustration on page 109 for clarification.

Remember that any combination of push and pull flaking can be used. Usually, a knapper gets into a particular habit and stays with it. Advanced pressure flaking techniques demand a full appreciation and command of the different modes of flaking. Switching back and forth is difficult and is something that aboriginal knappers didn't have to do. The danger lies in developing a habit strong enough that it precludes alternate styles of flaking.

One important difference between push and pull flaking is in the different requirements for platforms. Pull flaking is usually done with a sharp platform that digs into the tool and allows outward force. Push flaking, on the other hand, takes a well-built, sturdy platform that won't crush.

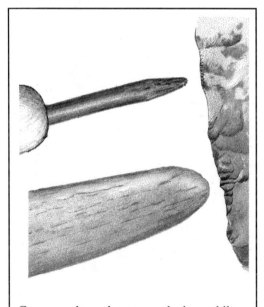

Copper tools work on ground edges while antler tools are best on spur platforms.

Rough edges that can be tolerated when using pull flaking are in sharp contrast to the carefully prepared platforms needed for push flaking.

The difference in platform types has an effect on tool use as well. Pull flaking takes a yielding tool tip, like antler, while the push method easily accommodates copper on a ground, beveled edge. Antler, seated on a well-ground edge, doesn't work easily in the push mode unless the platform has been isolated to ease release of the flake. A spur platform works by digging into the edge of the tool, which is then pushed so it grazes the preform surface. The same tool and platform can be used in the pull mode as well.

## EDITING YOUR RESULTS

Controlled flaking produces predictable flake trajectories. Yet many things can interfere with ideal results. Momentary relaxation in the push force may occur when the preform gives way, the tool vibrates, or when energy goes into a flaw. A flake that terminates by snapping at right angles to its path shows that there was a sudden increase in pull force that the trajectory could not adjust to and the flake broke by bending. Loss of the push component causes the pull component of force to direct the fracture toward the surface of the preform. If the push force is not recovered, the flake has a rounded end and it is called a hinged flake. If the interruption is slight, the push force turns the fracture back into the stone. Usually, once the balance of push and pull forces is disturbed, the flake trajectory continues to undulate back and forth across the ideal path. Pulling the tool outward while full compressive stress is in effect can cause the fracture to dive inward. Thin preforms are easily snapped in two this way.

The back and forth shifting in the knapping force causes ripples, or compression rings. The amplitude and frequency of the rings are a rough measure of the energy available during each stage of the flake advance. Amplitude (height of a wave) is a function of the size and duration of interruption, while frequency (space between two waves) is more closely related to available energy. Undulations are gentle and less frequent changes in the fracture trajectory, caused by mechanical imbalance. The difference between undulations and ripples is that ripples exist within and on undulations.

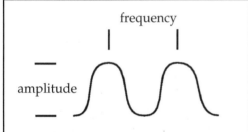

frequency

amplitude

A wave tells a story of forces at the fracture front shifting inward and outward as the fracture develops. Amplitude reveals how much disturbance is present and frequency tells how often it happens.

Analysts can tell a great deal about how energy has been applied by looking at the rises and falls in a flake scar. By noting where undulations begin, it is possible to tell if the knapper was never in control or simply lost it before the flake was finished. Relative spacing and size of undulations give good clues for determining which tools were used. Soft or limber tools allow more gentle changes in the fracture path than hard, stiff knapping tools because of the energy stored in compression of the tool.

Variations in the flake column cross-section due to flake geometry are often reflected as undulations. Since bending is proportional to thickness of the flake at each stage of the fracture, the direction of force at the fracture front is controlled to a degree by the shape of the surface. This is why Danish and Egyptian knappers ground their knife preform surfaces smooth before attempting to do precise ribbon flaking.

A fine, even set of compression rings is a sign of good knapping. Loss of control is rudely pointed out by the presence of severe ripples and undulations. Careful analysis of an undesirable result can often tell the knapper what was done wrong, and what might correct the problem. Learning to read the stone in this way really speeds up progress at mastering knapping skills. Deciphering the history of a prehistoric flake can also be a great help in designing or choosing an appropriate replication technique.

*Chapter 6*

# PERCUSSION

Everything I have written to this point has set the stage for the act of flintknapping. The concepts have been designed to approximate what the aboriginal knapper appreciated from experience and intuition. The particular combination of tool and muscle used for a specific result is called "technique." Unfortunately, we cannot capture the actions of the original knappers. Given the large number of tools and ways of manipulating them, the potential for variation is endless.

The best thing we can do for now is to describe techniques with which modern knappers have had the most success. Sometimes nearly identical results can be reached by techniques that seem far removed from each other. Once you understand the procedures that I describe, you can and should go your own direction. Do what works for you.

## QUARRYING

When Indians mined tabular stone, they extended and opened cracks by using wedges of wood and antler to obtain large chunks of stone. For cases where the stone was surrounded by another material, picks made of antler, bone, wood, or stone were used to worry the stone loose. Modern knappers can take significant shortcuts afforded by metal tools and mechanical equipment.

Mining was often a way to assure high quality stone. Stone that is exposed to the elements is subjected to all kinds of deterioration; toughening, drying, and severe cracking by repeated freezing and thawing. Mining with primitive tools takes a lot of work, but working with poor stone is equally frustrating.

The simplest method for reducing a large piece of mined stone is by throwing it against another hard rock. Throwing is especially useful to crack open a round rock. Australian aborigines did this and sorted through the scatter of debitage for suitable flakes.

Rounded cobbles can also be broken open by striking an oblique blow on their side. This is sometimes called quartering and works best if some small projection can be found on the cobble to carry the impact. Another means of opening a cobble is to hit it straight on, as it rests on an anvil. With a little luck, the cobble will be wedged in two. In most cases, you can expect some shattering with this method.

## CORE

Once the stone has at least one flat surface, other flakes can be taken. The techniques that may be used comprise what is known as *core technology*. The established surfaces serve as platforms from which large spalls of stone can be driven. There are two basic approaches. In the first, the core itself is thought of as the tool and the surrounding stone is removed as waste. This is called bifacing. In the second approach, the knapper creates flakes to be used as is, or further modified into tools, while the exhausted core is discarded.

There are several ways to take usable flakes off of cores. For very tough stone, like quartzite, it may work best to swing the core against a fixed anvil stone, using great power. This is a brute force technique not easy to control. Use it sparingly.

The primary method of core reduction is to hit the platform with a hammerstone. It sounds simple, but there are many variables to control. First, you must select a hammer that is as big or at least half as big as the flake. A hammer that is too small will bounce away before the flake can complete, and too large a hammer will shatter the core.

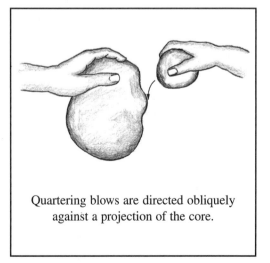

Quartering blows are directed obliquely against a projection of the core.

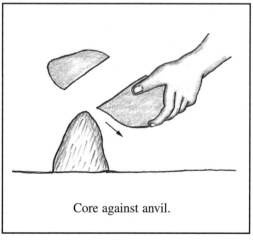

Core against anvil.

Study the available platform facets to find out where the edge forms an angle of slightly less than 90-degrees. Be careful when selecting an impact site. If the platform surface is too concave, the hammer will hit the wrong place. If the platform is too convex, the hammer will be apt to skid off. It is wise to be equally wary of flaws, humps, or depressions that lie in the path the flake is to take. Controlling as many conditions as you can gives you the best chance of making the flake you want.

It is also critical that the core be well supported. This does not mean you must absolutely immobilize it, quite the opposite. The best way to hold a large core in place is to set it in a loosely scuffed pile of dirt or sand. The core should be positioned so that the platform is nearly horizontal. Too solid a support can set up interfering counter forces and vibrations. Additional steadying by hand is all right as long as the blow feels crisp. When a blow feels cushioned or deadened, it will rarely produce a good flake. An excellent way of telling whether the blows are working is to listen to their sound. You want a clean snap. Once you have experienced that sound, you will have no trouble recognizing it.

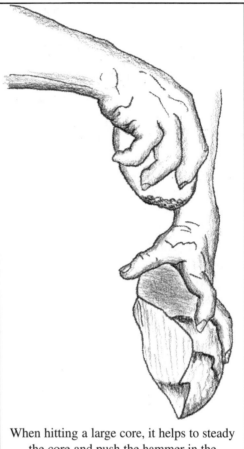

When hitting a large core, it helps to steady the core and push the hammer in the direction you want the stone to break.

Smaller cores (those less than a half-foot wide) can be rested on your thigh. The point at which you expect the fracture to emerge should be just slightly covered by the fleshy part of your leg. Use a leather pad to protect your leg. A perfectly removed flake will stay in place, held only by the slight support at the tip, because all the applied energy will have been used up by fracture.

Plan to strike at a point well in from the edge of the core. Think of it in terms of the width to thickness ratio of the flake. A flake destined to be made into a biface should be thick. If no further modification of the flake is planned, it may be possible to work close to the edge and get thinner flakes. As you work at the edge of the core, the edge and face should be cleaned off and stabilized by grinding to avoid shatter. This can reduce the force needed to remove a flake.

The hammer blow to the core should be crisp. If it bounces, the second contact can be disastrous. You can either pull the hammer away from the core on the rebound, or use a firm follow-through. Either way, the hammer should be gripped firmly and the swing should be as free from arm tension as possible.

Don't overpower the flake. If you use a large hammer, a slow blow may be sufficient to detach the flake without damage. A hammer that is too light has to be swung fast to have to detach the flake. This much energy risks shock and breakage. Properly balancing hammer weight and speed can result in percussion as gentle and controllable as pressure methods.

Direction of the blow can vary considerably depending on the tensile strength of the stone and the steepness of the platform. I normally like to keep the blow aligned with the flake axis. On tough stones, a glancing blow may be needed to get enough outward force to pull the flake loose. This outward force is best achieved by hitting well in from the edge of an inclined platform. In Europe, this approach is illustrated by the Clactonian technique. Resulting flakes are wide and thick.

## BLADES

Much longer and narrower flakes are possible when the blow is aligned with the flake. When the flake length exceeds twice the width, it is called a *blade* by European convention. Blades are tricky to make because they break so easily. If the cross-section can be kept uniform, there are fewer chances for errant forces to cause problems. The best way to control cross-section is to align the blade with one or more ridges from prior flakes. If no suitable straight ridge exists, it is possible to knap a close

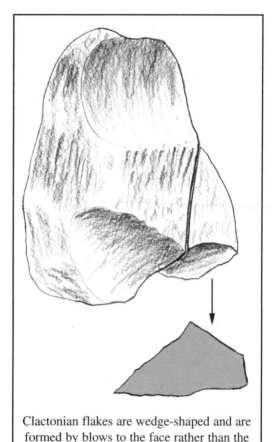

Clactonian flakes are wedge-shaped and are formed by blows to the face rather than the edge.

approximation by alternating blows from side to side so that a narrow, sinuous guiding edge is created. The first blow along the just built ridge creates a crested blade or *lame à crête*.

As soon as the first blade has been removed, two more guiding ridges are available for subsequent blades. If the core has the right shape, the progression of blades can completely encircle it. Once the first set of blades has been removed, the next set will tend to run straighter because there are fewer irregularities in the cross-section to divert the force as the fracture extends. Situating the impact between two ridges creates a blade with a trapezoidal cross-section.

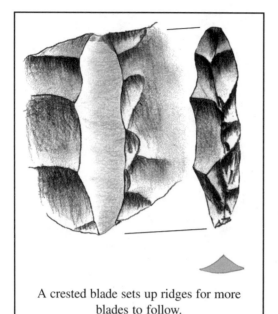

A crested blade sets up ridges for more blades to follow.

Flake-blades are not easy to modify bifacially and were usually used as is. It is therefore prudent to control thickness and trajectory carefully. What you get is what you use, and you want to get a *lot* of useable flakes out of a core. Striking a point some distance from the edge can produce thicker blades. A more precise method is to bevel the edge so a blow on the edge causes a flake to penetrate a prescribed distance from the core face. The bevel serves the additional function of making the flake more flexible, which allows it to travel further. Trajectory is a function of the balance of forces, so rocking the core curves the blade, while straight blades come from immobile cores.

Keeping blades intact can be a major problem. I find that a gentle support along the *entire* blade length helps to avoid snapping by lessening outward forces. Using a slow blow and a soft hammer also helps by reducing shock. A hard blow will send a compression wave down the slender

blade with a tension zone in its wake. All too often, the tension is enough to break a blade.

A related technique was used for flake-blades at the end of the Neolithic in central France. Archaeologists call it *Livre de burre* or "pound of butter" due to the shape of the core. This involves using deeply troughed, regularly spaced percussion flakes to make a long, thick lenticular biface tapered to each end. Two flakes at one end create a ridge for a striking platform perpendicular to the core face. The resulting long blade may be used as a dagger. Since the ridge-platform is delicate and shows little damage, many analysts assume the hammer to have been wood or antler. The real answer remains open to re-discovery.

It is generally assumed that flake-blade techniques maximize the usable working edge available from a given volume of stone. Understand, however, that blade technologies are also associated with large quantities of available stone. Where stone was sparse, or found only in small pieces, a preference for bifacial strategies developed to extract the largest tool from a given piece of stone. Blade making is less likely to have developed as a measure of efficiency in the use of stone, than as a luxury made possible by plenty. In most parts of the world, the development of bifacial strategies was founded on a need to make the most of limited resources.

## BIFACE

Any time both faces of the object of percussion are modified to make a tool, the result is called a biface. A core can also be a biface if it is shaped and used. Conversely, a biface is also a core, if the flakes from its face are destined for another purpose.

A biface can start as a large piece taken from a core, or it can be any piece of found stone. No matter the original form, biface technologies involve edging, shaping, and thinning the parent stone. You can generally use the same tools as those used for cores. The difference is that bifaces are usually smaller than cores and have sharper edges. Batons and softer hammerstones are preferred over hard hammers for working on delicate edges.

The first thing to master in bifacial technology is edging. In general, at least part of the preform edge is square or rounded. It is difficult to work effectively on a square edge, so some way has to be found to make the obstacle less difficult. The solution is to find an acute enough edge to allow flakes to be removed and to use blows alternate from one face to the other to "sew" an edge through the problem area. Each blow is struck just at the edge of the trough of an earlier flake scar.

When the stone is thick to start with, it may be better to concentrate on thinning than on edging. An effective means for rapid thinning is to treat the biface as a Levallois core, like the illustration on page 9. In this case, the thick flake is planned for the surface it leaves behind, and not for use of itself. Usually, the edge of the preform is beveled to provide a series of platforms. Three or four well-chosen flakes can flatten the biface.

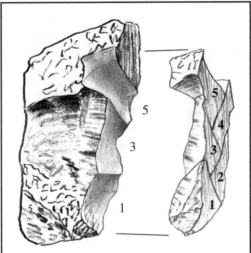

Square edges can be removed by "sewing," with flakes taken alternately from either face.

Edging and thinning are most effective when they are coordinated. Whenever possible, thinning should be done first. Edging follows much more easily when the thick parts of the biface have been removed. It is helpful to think of edging as preparation of platforms for operations to follow. When a platform suitable for thinning presents itself, the thinning flake should be removed immediately. If you wait, you take the chance of losing the platform when the edging is continued. Throughout the process, it is important to clearly visualize the tool still buried in the stone. The developing edge should keep to the projected center plane. Otherwise, an unsightly bow or twist will be left in the finished product. The same problem can develop if thinning flakes are not planned for their relation to the edge plane of the finished artifact. It is the same as a sculptor removing superfluous bits of stone until only the statue inside is left.

A handy trick is to pick the face which is already flattest and flake it as flat as possible. Then turn the preform over and work the second face into a parallel plane. At this stage, it is relatively easy to go ahead with final thinning and shaping. This method of working one face at a time was exploited by Clovis toolmakers.

One kind of percussion flake merits special attention. Tranchet flakes, like overshot flakes, would be considered an error in most contexts because they peel off an edge. The idea of squaring an edge when you have been trying hard to make edges sharp seems like undoing your efforts, but there are times when it makes sense. Burins are made with a special form of tranchet flake to create a square edge. The square, chisel-like edge was a favored tool for carving wood and bone. Another use of the tranchet flake is to develop a convenient surface to use as a platform for core blades, particularly when the old surface is damaged. Sometimes it means striking a layer off the top of the core, called a core tablet. When the tranchet flake has a strong curve or wrap-around effect, it is often called an orange peel flake. Special attention must be given to the balance of forces in order to control the fracture trajectory.

## PLATFORMS

Placement of the platform is important for control of the character of the biface. The impact site should be near the face you want to thin and away from the center plane to allow good fracture travel and create flat faces. Striking near the center plane greatly increases the chance of breakage from bending. However, either slight lift or give of the preform edge can allow the knapper to strike the center plane and precisely control lenticular shapes.

Clovis and Folsom workers tended to bevel an entire edge at once, since several flakes were to be taken from the same face before turning the preform over. A few blows at widely spaced intervals can clean off the entire face. Other cultures such as Cody for example, liked to use an individually prepared platform for each blow. Both approaches work, but there were decided cultural preferences.

A special treatment of the edge, unique to the Clovis culture, prepares an entire edge at once as a platform that can be struck anywhere you choose. Clovis knappers would batter with a hammerstone straight into the entire edge and then grind it thoroughly. As you might expect, this causes numerous incipient fractures that penetrate the edge and allow a fracture to start easily. If you simply grind the edge without battering it, flakes will be harder to remove and smaller.

More frequently, you need to isolate percussion platforms rather than use the whole edge because the preform is too small or too irregular. You can use small flakes to create a small trough on either side of the impact site, and leave it sticking slightly out from the rest of the edge. It also helps to stabilize the platform by grinding it. Force from the blow will be contained along a prescribed portion of the edge.

Failure to adequately prepare a platform is sure to disappoint you. The problems include crushing, hinge fracturing, preform breakage, and chattering to mention but a few. This is a common bane to the novice who tries to take shortcuts. Even the expert hesitates to take a shortcut when it comes to platform preparation.

## SUPPORT

Since biface geometry is influenced more by the method of support than any other variable, it deserves special consideration. There are many choices available for the support of a biface as it is being worked. I use the top of my leg as a yielding anvil for the heavy flaking stages, but switch to freehand support as soon as I no longer need as much power to get the results I want. Some knappers will keep the preform against their leg for every stroke. You need to decide what is best for you.

Good support becomes more critical as preform thickness is reduced. Low ratios of width to thickness, and width to length make the preform easy to break by shock and bending. Be especially careful that the ends of the preform are uniformly supported. For long preforms, the outside of the thigh gives about a foot of linear support. At least a half-foot of even support

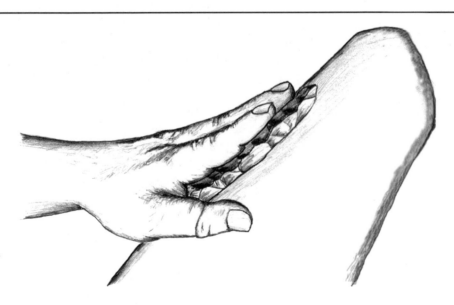

Knappers view of pressing a large biface against the outside of your thigh to reduce bend breakage during percussion. Be sure to provide heavy padding to help absorb the force of your blow as it follows through against your leg.

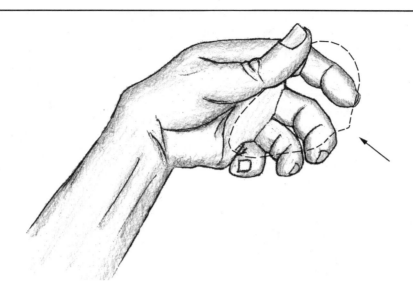

Note how the fingers are spread to distribute support evenly for freehand baton percussion. The thumb steadies the preform gently without squeezing it. When the preform is situated properly, a blow can be directed onto a platform between the first two fingers.

is available by simply resting the preform on an outstretched hand. A common mistake is to try supporting both faces at once. This causes opposing forces are built up, which allows bend breakage and overshots. While just laying a preform on top of your palm doesn't seem steady, energy from a properly delivered blow is so well absorbed by fracture that not enough remains to throw the preform off the support, even if it is lying loose.

Decisions of how to hold the biface should take into account the kind of cross-section you want to achieve. Flat, parallel faces are most easily obtained when the support is flat and held still. By slightly lifting the edge being struck, you can cause flakes to curve across the face. Allowing the preform to give slightly as it is hit can result in a nearly diamond-shaped cross-section.

Blows along the center plane should be especially loose, to keep from breaking the preform in two. A different kind of breakage occurs if the impact is far from the center plane. Any counter force by the support on the opposite edge can cause an overshot flake, which peels off the far edge. That is why you need to rotate the biface by lifting the edge closest to you—not by levering from the rear edge.

If you desire especially flat faces, you can obtain a slight advantage in energy transfer by allowing the rear edge of the biface to drive directly against the long axis of a finger. With a raised platform and a straight-in blow, flakes can carry extremely far and flat. For maximum effect, flakes should be spaced so they just overlap. The wide spacing of impact sites has an added benefit of creating plane faces which, in turn, results in an even thickness along the length of the preform. By setting a flake you have just removed alongside its scar, you can mark an impact site that gives the widest flake spacing with minimum overlap of scars.

Though it's not usually wise to support both faces at the same time, a special trick can be used to get a deeply penetrating, flat flake. Try lightly pinching the preform at the center between thumb and forefinger. A soft, thick pad should be wadded beneath the preform. This padding allows flakes to carry flat, past the center, with smooth terminations. If the support is exactly in the center, even a bad blow will be forgiven because the preform will rotate freely out of the way.

Another technique may be called for if the stone breaks too easily in tension. It is possible to use friction to force the stone into compression by pulling on the underside with the fingertips while bracing the rear edge. The force is not large, but can be just enough to allow the flake to shear free without breaking the preform. It takes a lot of practice to master this technique.

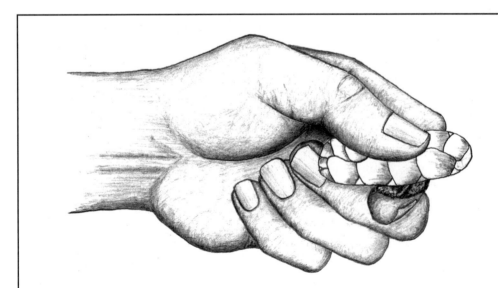

Pinching the preform near its center, with a soft leather pad wadded underneath allows delicate percussion thinning without much danger of breakage.

## BATONS

There are many different ways of wielding a baton. Only you can determine the best way for yourself. You are likely to find that particular effects are associated with particular modes of operation. Holding the baton at the end, like a hammer, is generally the most comfortable. Contact with the stone may either be in line with or perpendicular to the baton axis, depending on how much energy you need from the mass of the hammer. Sometimes, the baton is most effective when held near its contact end, like a hammerstone. I can't over-emphasize the importance of finding a comfortable mode of delivery can not be overemphasized. I switch positions frequently to achieve an effect, but just as often to relieve the stress that the blows transmit to my body. When I experience a severe case of "knappers elbow" during a demonstration, I find that I get good results with percussion by raising my elbow and swinging my forearm like a pendulum. The lesson is not only how to be more comfortable, but the easy blow can be highly effective.

With most techniques, the best kind of a blow uses a very loose grip on the baton. An isolated, well-ground platform insures that you will hit the right place and reduces the force needed to detach the flake. You can make very small bifaces this way, but the real utility of the method is the efficiency with which irregularities can be cleaned off a preform in the early stages.

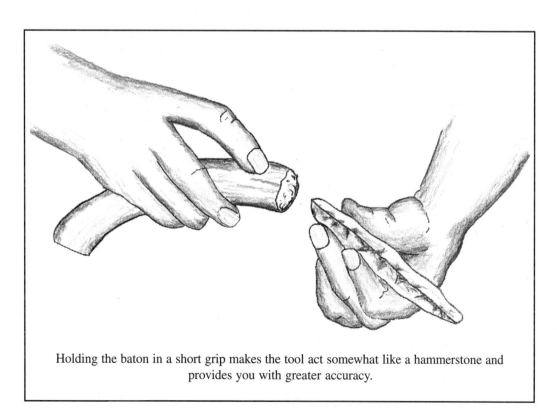

Holding the baton in a short grip makes the tool act somewhat like a hammerstone and provides you with greater accuracy.

Beginning knappers find it difficult to hit accurately, especially with heavy or fast blows. You have to expect new motor skills to take some time to develop, but I can offer at least one helpful hint. Try cocking your wrist back and spinning the baton about your thumb. This allows you to hit with great speed while using a short blow. Heavy batons are easiest to use in this manner. Since you are not swinging your whole arm, it is easy to make the blow land on target.

Shaping is an integral part of the bifacing process. By the time the desired thickness is reached, the outline should also be well established. Just be sure that enough material is left for pressure retouching. Good percussion leaves a clean, uniform surface without significant hollows or bumps. The best percussion work needs only light pressure retouch to create a finished tool.

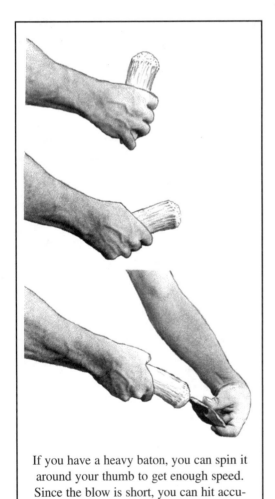

If you have a heavy baton, you can spin it around your thumb to get enough speed. Since the blow is short, you can hit accurately as well.

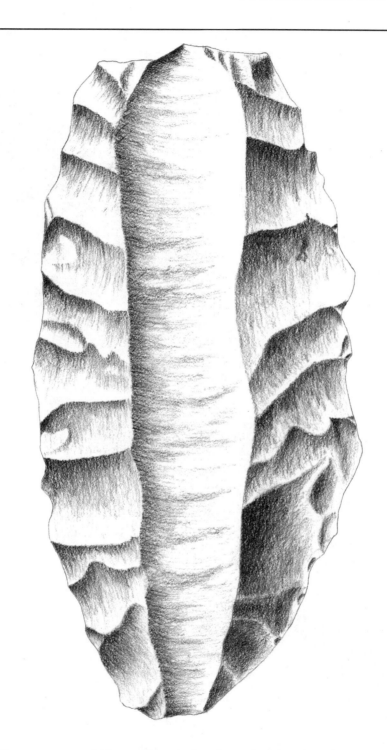

Pound of butter cores are debitage. The actual tool was the 25-cm long flake from the face. After Peter Kelterborn, <u>The Livre de burre Method</u>, Flintknappers' Exchange, Vol 4, No 3, 1981

This 10.5-inch Solutrian biface from France was made by baton percussion, and cached some 15,000 to18,000 years ago. The face illustrated is nearly concave, while the reverse is slightly convex. Maximum thickness, near the top end, is only 7.7-mm.

*Chapter 7*

# PRESSURE

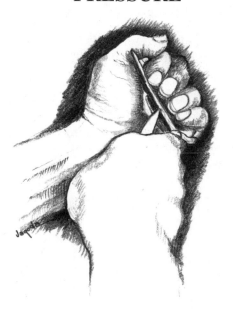

No matter how well percussion is done, subtle refinements by pressure can improve the tool. In fact, the most common use of pressure is to trim a percussion preform. If the thickness and cross-section are already suitable, there is no need for flakes to carry very far in from the edge. In this case, it is often sufficient to set it on a flat surface, prop the edge up, and press flakes off the edge with an antler tine. The result is an inelegant but effective beveled edge.

Most people who get involved with knapping are interested in using pressure to modify and pattern the entire face of the preform. While this is reasonable and achievable, it requires complex techniques. Proper support of the preform and use of tools is difficult to describe and takes practice to learn. Relatively few archaeological samples show evidence of patterned flake scars made by pressure.

Beginners often find that the flake will not come off no matter how hard they push. This usually occurs because the applied forces are directed into the body of the stone rather than skimming the surface. If you have this kind of problem, review the principles of force balance described in chapter 5, in relation to pressure methods of knapping.

## TOOLS

Modern knappers often use copper-tipped tools for at least two good reasons. Copper is easy to obtain and it offers excellent control. Some native cultures are well documented as having used copper tools, but antler tines or bone were a much more common choice. A pressure tool has to be hard and strong, but still allow an edge of stone to indent it. Copper takes less maintenance than antler and is more durable on a fine tip. Just use care when using copper on delicate edges.

## SUPPORT

I hesitate to say much about tools or methods for holding tools and preforms, as it often boils down to personal preferences or strength. Beginners often lever the presser with their thumb, but it doesn't take long for that to become painful. I person-ally prefer using the base of my forefinger to bear the brunt of the pressure. A potential drawback is that strong wrist action is needed. You can try gripping the antler in your fist like a dagger. By throwing your shoulder into the action, tremendous controlled force can be generated.

When doing pressure work it is absolutely critical to support the preform evenly. Most breakage in the pressure stage is caused by bending due to bridging on either side of the pressure point. The most basic support is a wedge of leather or wood used to elevate the edge away from a leg or table. Flakes tend to travel progressively farther the closer the face can be aligned to the direction of force. Advanced knappers usually hold the preform in their hand with a pad of rubber or leather for protection. The best way to get a flat, working support is to keep your thumb in line with the back of your hand. Anchor the preform against

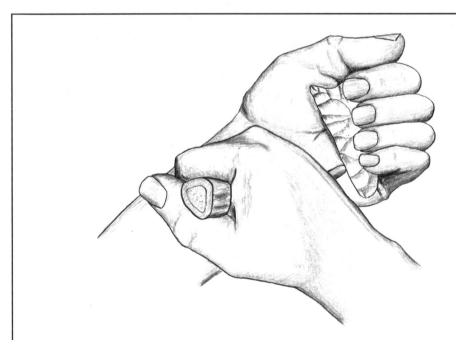

Holding the pressor like a dagger works aids heavy flaking if you throw your shoulder foward to bring weight to bear through the tool.

the crease across the middle of your palm. Follow-through by the presser tip is best absorbed by the fleshy part of the heel of your hand. You can hold the preform in place with your fingertips and rock the working edge up by pushing down the rear edge.

Another way of changing the angle of approach is to cock your supporting wrist back. Since this can be a difficult position to maintain, it is usually good to brace your wrist in position against your leg. If you are sitting, you can brace your presser arm against the other leg for increased power.

The way you set up your platform is critical. Edges tend to be sharp and fragile during the pressure stage. Working directly on these edges can ruin a presser tip and damage the stone edge so badly that further progress is impossible. Often, it is sufficient to abrade the edge lightly with a rough stone. At times, steep bevels are helpful in making the edge strong enough to withstand the percussion tool. For an especially high degree of control, small spur platforms can be built in imitation of percussion techniques. The spur is impressed in the tip of the presser before full pressure is applied. As the flake comes off, it behaves as an extension of the presser. I use spur platforms for most of my patterned flaking. Because the spur distributes stress, a blunt presser tool tip can be used to obtain delicate results.

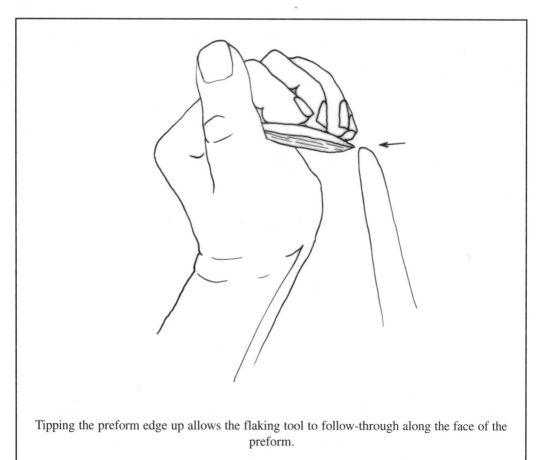

Tipping the preform edge up allows the flaking tool to follow-through along the face of the preform.

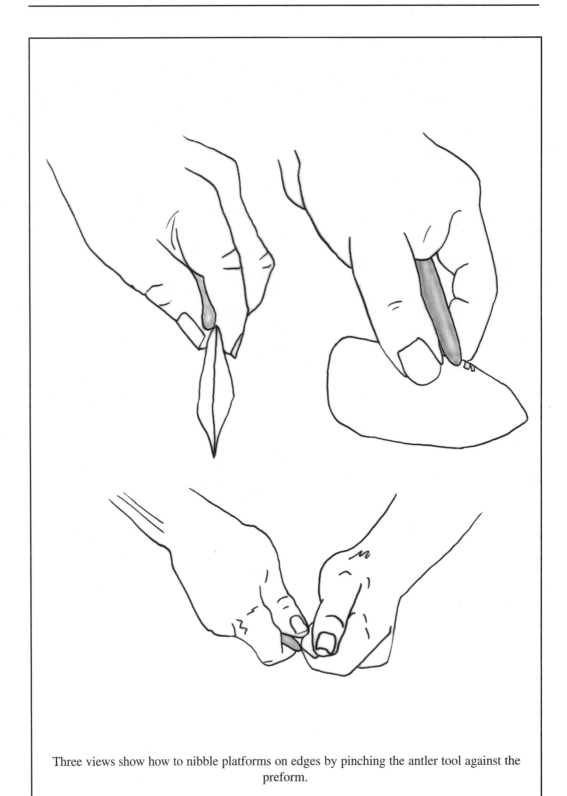

Three views show how to nibble platforms on edges by pinching the antler tool against the preform.

## CONTROL OF FLAKE SCARS

When you use a broad, spatulate presser tip, you don't need as strong an edge because the force is distributed. It is necessary to work against a straight edge to avoid spotty contact with the edge. This method produces broad, shallow flake scars suitable for Agate Basin-style replicas. Follow-through in the pull mode of flaking helps to avoid snagging the edge with the tool and adds to the penetrating qualities of the flake.

Attempts to extend the flake very far in relation to its width must take the balance of forces into account, not only to start the flake, but also to carry it along. Large compressive stresses are necessary to ensure that a fracture stays on course. The surest way of realizing a proper balance is to feel it. To do that, try anchoring the butt of the presser against the heel of your hand. Now, when the tool is out of alignment, obvious corrective action is required to be able to knap.

The trajectory taken by a pressure flake depends on the balance of forces. A hand-held system is inherently unstable and difficult to control. Blocks and wedges help to make the direction of force constant for each flake. This is especially important in Eden style flaking. Taking arced flakes presents another problem that is not so easily solved.

The direction of force needs to change if you want the fracture to arc over the face of the preform. Many knapping styles have been developed toward this end, but they all take some skill. One solution is to move support of the preform to its rear edge, allowing it to rock. As the flake comes off, the preform rocks up and lets the flake curve. The direction of pressure at the tool tip is nearly constant in this case. Another possibility is to use wrist action to rock the preform upwards while the presser is being similarly manipulated downwards.

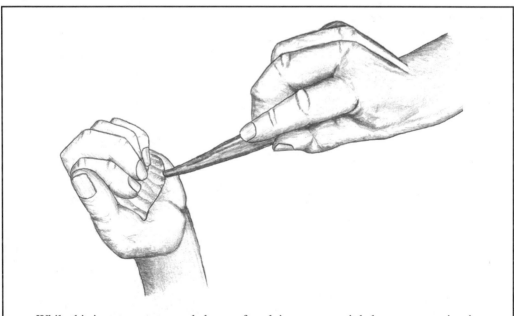

While this is not a recommended way of applying pressure, it helps you recognize the importance of balancing push and pull forces.

One problem common to the above techniques is that the flakes may overshoot and ruin the far edge. As in percussion, one remedy lies in keeping pressure off the far edge. Another is to avoid letting flakes penetrate deeply into the preform by making sure the platform is not too strong. There is no foolproof way to avoid overshot. It is up to the individual to develop skill by experience.

Geometry of flake scars is controlled to some extent by the components of force. Force aligned with a flake tends to leave parallel-sided scars. If the force has a large outward (pull) component, the scar tends to widen as it goes. Another way to influence the shape of flake scars is by the effect the surface has on the flake. When a flake is directed down a ridge, it stays narrow. By deliberately making each flake follow the ridge left by a previous flake, it is easy to build a pattern of parallel scars. Such a succession of flakes can be used to make a uniform surface. If the progression of flaking is in the same direction as the slant of the flakes, the scars that remain have a weak inclination.

The way to get strongly slanted scars is to progress away from the direction of force. Slanting the flake has the effect of flattening the arc over which the flake has to travel. Overall, the technique allows the greatest thickness feasible where flakes cross the centerline. Some of the old Paleo-period parallel flaked points have remarkably thick cross-sections for strength.

Patterned flaking is almost always serial; that is, each flake is removed adjacent to the preceding flake. It is more usual to see each flake being selectively positioned to shape, edge, and thin the artifact, or to remove a flaw. Selective flaking leaves scars with widely divergent shapes and sizes. Sometimes the term "random flaking" is used, but that implies a complete lack of plan. I think saying "flaking was selectively applied" better represents a craftsman's intent than saying, "this point was flaked at random."

Serial flakes make parallel scar patterns.
Note the platform for the next flake.

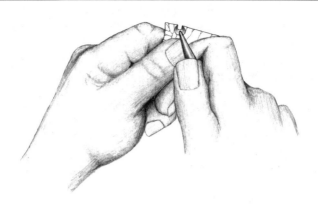

Slide-away notching requires a steady build-up of pressure just in from the notch edge. Follow-through must be slight, or you will split the preform.

## NOTCHING

Simple notching is basically an extension of edge dressing. The difference is merely that you stay in the same place, while alternating flakes from one face to the other. A spatulate tool used on edge allows you to make a narrow notch. By squaring the bottom of the notch between successive flakes, you can avoid binding. Each flake should remove a small crescent. Too deep a bite causes the crescent to expand into a cone, which can pop off the ears or tang of the artifact. Special methods are needed for extra-long or thin notches.

One slick method of deep notching is to use a conical tip of copper pointing from the center of the artifact to the edges. A steady build-up of pressure causes a neat semi-circular flake to pop out of the underside of the notch. This is termed the slide-away method because of the odd direction in which the tool points. I have seen some amazing dogleg notches done this way.

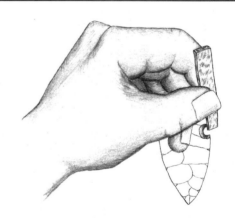

A slim, copper punch can be effective for deep notching. The tip should be squared and barely engage the notch edge.

Another deep-notching method also uses copper. A square-ended punch of flattened copper can cut notches an inch and a half deep by an eighth-inch wide. The punch is rested vertically so that it barely laps into the notch. A sharp blow does the trick. Between blows, the notch end needs to be squared so the punch doesn't bind. Don't get in a rush and try punching too deep at a time. The result can be a huge flake that is apt to take the ears of the point with it. Some knappers have been quite successful at punching with antler notchers. They take lots of care in maintaining the tool tip to avoid binding or other damage.

Although I haven't tried them, toothed notchers made of copper found in the Mississippi Valley combine pressure with percussion for notching. The end of a copper rod is flattened and squared. Square notches are filed into the end so that three teeth are left. To use the tool, press the tool on edge very firmly in the hollow of the notch and slide it outwards. When it drops over the edge, the next tooth strikes the notch in a mini-percussion blow and advances the notch.

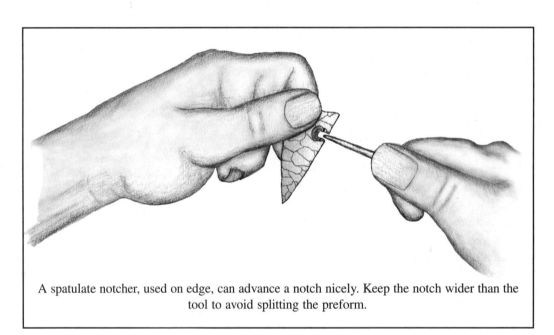

A spatulate notcher, used on edge, can advance a notch nicely. Keep the notch wider than the tool to avoid splitting the preform.

*Chapter 8*

# THE ALL—IMPORTANT FLAKE

A flake is the primary unit of reduction in flintknapping. Flakes make edges, thin preforms, shape tools, and contour surfaces. They can also be useful in their own right as blanks, ready for making into tools, or directly as knives, projectile points, and scrapers. This chapter will explore the importance of various flake uses and explain flake formation by looking at how forces inside the stone influence the shape of a flake. Don't let the technical language bog you down, the next chapter gives you simple recipes for making spear points.

When you can control the form of a flake, you have control over what stone tools you can make and how they will look. Primitive people knew exactly what they were trying to achieve, and the modern student is well advised to become just as sensitive to the many nuances of flakes.

Archeologists have described and named a number of flake types. Unfortunately we tend to see them in the context of a particular place and time, and too often fail to recognize the same flake type in a different context. The problem is partly one of vocabulary. For example, there is not a common understanding of what is meant by a Clactonian flake, because it was intended to describe a particular style common to an area in England about 300,000 years ago. Therefore, I will try to avoid using terms like Clactonian to characterize broad categories, although they are useful as illustrative examples. We must talk about any kind of flake clearly and unambiguously, whether it has been described formally or not.

## FLAKE FUNCTIONS

A flintknapper must be able to clearly determine what kind of flake is needed for a given situation and how to make it. Examples of flake uses show that there are many ways to reach an objective and the same kind of flake can serve many purposes. If you can make every flake do what you want, then chances are good the replication will be suitable. I will discuss six basic functions that flakes perform, along with three episodes of flake formation, and numerous attributes that can be quantified for ready comparison to archaeological samples.

Too often, I see beginners destroy valuable stone because they aren't willing to evaluate each stroke for its contribution to the whole. Flakes do not just happen, they must be struck according to a predetermined plan, with the right tool, using the right technique, and in the right direction. You can see that making a flake requires thought.

The best way to learn to control flakes is to sketch on the preform where you expect the flake to go, and see how well your flake can match your prediction. It is a tedious process, but you need to understand why a flake did or did not go where you expected while you can still remember everything you did to make it. Another benefit of this practice is that you become very familiar with the shapes your flakes take, which allows you to place them most effectively. Eventually, you will not need a pencil to predict your flakes but keep up the practice of mentally reviewing your degree of control.

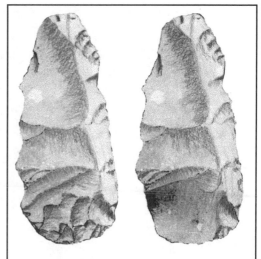

An orange peel flake can be used to put a sharp edge on an adze.

### Make an Edge

When a flake is formed, its perimeter is sharp and another sharp edge is left where it detaches from the parent core. It is important to take into account the function of the edge you want to form. Do you want an uninterrupted, razor-like edge, or will a serrated edge be better? Flakes that form the working tool edge are called edging flakes. Several flakes struck in succession usually leave a ragged edge. Trimming off the overhang bounding a bulbar scar, while preparing the next adjacent flake platform, can minimize rough edges. If you want a sharp, unbroken edge, you can send a flake along an edge by an oblique blow. Edges can also be improved by choosing a technique that minimizes bulbar scars and troughs. In percussion, this means using a fast blow and broad contact. Push mode pressure flaking also helps keep edges clean.

Sometimes you want to build a tool with steep edges. At other times you might need thin, acute edges. Thin, sharp edges result naturally from thinning flakes. Moving the platform towards the center of the preform can cause edge angles to be steep. You can sometimes control the edge angle of a core by the direction of the blow, but only if you hold the hammer tightly.

Waste flakes from edging a biface can be recognized from the remnants of previous edges they retain. Platform faceting or grinding are the most common clues to what the previous edge looked like, but overshot terminations on waste flakes preserve substantial sections of edge for archaeologists to study.

*Examples: overshot, burin, tranchet (slice), orange peel flake, core tablet, platform, polish on scraper retouch flakes, bevel*

### Shape a Tool

Shaping is usually associated with edging or thinning. The worker should have a good idea of what he is trying to accomplish, and can place edging and thinning blows where they will also be of most benefit to the final shape. It is generally not a good practice to establish shape before the other flaking modes are attempted because you limit your options. Final shaping is almost always the last action other than setting up the required edge, and often is a part of edging. When the scars that result from shaping reach the edge, it is because they were applied late in the process. Notching and insets for hafting are part of shaping, and the flakes tend to be rather steep. Shaping at an intermediate stage of work may be recognized by an interruption of the face plane. When a flake doesn't appear to thin, contour, or edge, it probably was meant to shape.

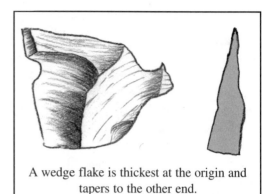

A wedge flake is thickest at the origin and tapers to the other end.

When the main intent is to shape, the flake is usually thick and short, with little regard for edge refinement beyond leaving enough material for another type of flake to be taken. Wedge flakes are good for major shaping, but offer little control of edging or thinning. Wedge flakes can be made in the Clactonian manner by striking a blow somewhat in from the acute edge of a core or preform, to form a flake that is wedge shaped in profile, as illustrated on page 56.

Most shaping flakes are unstructured, and probably were not used for other purposes—in other words, they are clearly what we call debitage or waste flakes. Some are wedge shaped, but it is also common to gradually reach the shape of the tool by using thin, scalar flakes. When you shear an edge by pressing it with the side of your tool, scalar flakes are thrown off.

*Examples: Clactonian, scalar, wedge flake*

### Improve Surface Contour

Surfaces nearly always need to be flattened, rounded, or made smoother, for a tool to serve its function well. Sometimes the surface improvement takes the form of aesthetic patterning effects. When you look at debitage, contouring flakes are often recognized by the fact that they intersect step fractures or remove surface flaws. Flakes that improve surface contour tend to have variable thickness, not to be confused with variations caused by undulations. Contouring flake scars can be defined as those that reach at least halfway to the center of the preform. The scars from contouring flakes on an artifact are often isolated from the edge by subsequent edging flakes.

Ribbon flakes are useful for making pleasing scar patterns.

To flatten a surface, you want a flake that expands rapidly with a minimum of bulbar swelling. To be of most use, a flattening flake should be free of undulations and terminate smoothly. Sometimes a high velocity blow helps make a flatter flake. Solutrean laurel leaf knives are a good example of effective flattening, but look at the biface at the end of chapter 12

for the ultimate in thin and flat.

*Examples: ribbon, Lame à crête, overshot*

### Thin a Tool

Thinning requires that flakes must travel past the thick portions of the preform surface. Every culture had a preference for how thick a tool should be to perform its intended task, based on their experience of how vulnerable the tool was to damage. The tool is not complete until enough stone is removed to reach the target thickness.

Flakes intended for thinning need stable platforms to carry heavy blows. Levallois-like flakes are ideal for thinning at early stages because you have a nearly square platform and the fracture travels all the way to the opposite edge. True Levallois flakes were not designed for thinning. Rather, the flake was destined to be a fully shaped tool by its detachment from a core, which had a carefully shaped surface. However, there is no reason not to take advantage of the technique for the thickness it removes as well as for the surface it leaves.

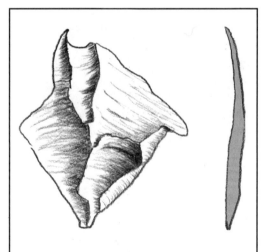

A potato chip flake is not a formal type, but provides a helpful analogy.

Thinning flakes tend to have uniform shape and thickness and they almost always extend past opposing scar terminations. Low angle scars remaining from earlier stages generally indicate thinning flakes.

*Examples: overshot, channel flake, bipolar, potato chip flake (broad, thin), Levallois*

### Use as a tool or as a blank

A flake destined for later use as a tool is considered a blank. A blank was almost always designed to be thicker than the purpose it was being created for would dictate. The reason is that most techniques are not reliable enough to avoid making the flake too thin to function properly. In this case, economy is best served by planning to waste some thickness.

While most flakes converted to tools seem to have been scavenged from debitage, a notable exception is in the use of deliberate overshot flakes to create flakes that would serve as scrapers. The Cody culture combined objectives during the production of projectile preforms. An overshot flake served the purpose of making a blank for a scraper at the same time it contoured the surface of a preform. Often, the overshot even converted a square edge opposite the one being worked on to a sharp edge.

Quartering or bipolar blows are most common for making blanks because the wedging flake initiation minimizes bulb formation and promotes a straight fracture path. It sometimes takes a large hammer or a firm grip on the hammer to provide enough effective mass. It is also necessary to strike in a plane well above the core edge so that the flake will have enough thickness that material can be removed and still make another tool.

Archeological collections usually do not contain many flakes that were obviously intended as blanks, because those flakes already had been made into tools. Some of the blanks I have seen were apparently collected as naturally occurring flakes. Generally, the most massive example of a blank is a quartering flake, where a large cobble is broken into sections. Often a cobble was exploited solely for flakes that could be used as tools. Flake tools made from cobbles tend to retain their cortex, and they often are made of different stone than bifaces.

Flakes intended to be used as tools in their own right are designed or chosen for their shape and symmetry as well as for their degree of curvature. Steep edge angles are typical because of the stability they provide, but sometimes it is the sharp, acute edges that are sought.

*Examples: Levallois, blade, micro-blade, core, blank, Pound of Butter, Mousterian*

**79**

### Unit of damage

We have talked so far about flakes that resulted from planned action, but archeology is full of examples of flakes caused by accident. The accident may be a mistake during production of the tool, or it can result from use of the tool.

Projectile points that strike a hard object often have a characteristic impact flake removed from the tip. Less obvious damage includes shatter from tool or target, bend-induced scaling of flakes from the edge of a scraping tool, breaks caused by objects falling on the tool, or treading on the tool after it has been used. If you are doing archaeological analysis, it is important to know when a fracture happens. Unfortunately it can be tricky to spot the clues that reveal when events happened relative to each other. Sometimes, use wear or patination shows the passage of time.

Since this point was found in soft soil, we assume that it impacted against bone.

Some types of fracture are more common in inadvertent breaks than they are in deliberate ones. For example, impact breaks show severe undulations caused by excess energy and inability to control how force is applied. Tools that are broken by stepping on them or levered in two have right-angled breaks that flex as they reach the far edge. Misdirected blows can create perverse, spiral shaped breaks that angle from the edge.

*Examples: Impact flake, shatter*

## HOW A FLAKE IS FORMED

From a mechanical standpoint, knapping fracture is caused by tensile stress arising from shear or bending. Stone is roughly 50 times weaker in tension than in compression, and fails in tension more quickly than in any other mode of stress. Compression and shear seldom play a direct role in separating a flake from a stone core because stones usually resist until a catastrophic failure occurs. It is a fact of physics that the major stress of tension is at right angles to the minor stress of compression. That means that when a blow applies compression, the tension that pries off the flake is perpendicular to the force of the stroke. Unlike regularly-shaped building components that are engineered with predictable loads, complex shapes of rocks introduce stress in ways we can't predict. Even so, it is possible to consider the development of fracture in three episodes: initiation, propagation, and termination.

### Platforms

Before we get too involved with following the fracture that detaches a flake, we should talk briefly about where the blow lands. The impact site, or platform, has much to do with how force is transmitted into the stone. Impact on a flat surface is the most straightforward and simple case because stress develops in largely predictable ways. Platforms with multiple facets are less reliable because you don't know just where the tool will contact. When platforms are isolated, they allow the impact to be precisely positioned and concentrated. Extreme concentration of force is provided by a spur platform.

### Initiation

At fracture initiation, energy is delivered to the stone by direct contact of a tool. Depending on the tool, the nature of the platform, and the support provided, a crack initiates in one of three modes: Hertzian cone, bend, or wedge. The different modes of initiation rely more on the relative hardness of the hammer than on how fast force is delivered as their primary cause.

### *Hertzian cone*

True conchoidal flakes can only form by the impact of a relatively hard hammer. A blow perpendicular to a flat surface compresses the stone until a shallow ring crack, seldom more than a millimeter deep, forms around the area of contact. It then flares between 70 and 130-degrees in a cone that is 3 or 4 times as deep as the diameter of the initial ring crack. For a classic example of a Hertzian cone, look at your windshield when a pebble makes a direct hit. A flintknapper normally strikes so close to the edge that the cone is seldom complete. Outward bending moves the crack back toward the free face and forms what is

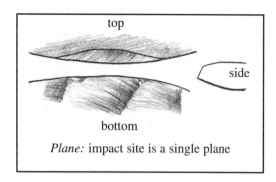

*Plane:* impact site is a single plane

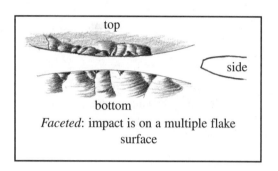

*Faceted*: impact is on a multiple flake surface

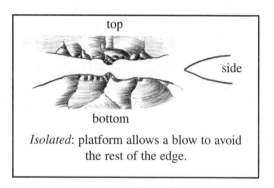

*Isolated*: platform allows a blow to avoid the rest of the edge.

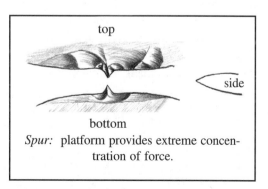

*Spur:* platform provides extreme concentration of force.

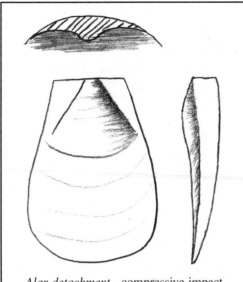

*Alar detachment* - compressive impact followed by bending, primarily hard hammer, characterized by a salient bulbar swelling.

### Wedge initiation

If the force that creates a Hertzian cone is not allowed to rebound, enough stress may exist to split the cone by a wedging action. When the force is increased after the cone has grown three to four times the diameter of the original ring crack, stone directly beneath the cone flows plastically and opens a crack in the middle of the cone. Since the cone is split, there can be no bulb of force, although shatter is often significant because of the high level of stress.

Wedging can also be caused when the blow collapses weak zones in the stone or drives debris into existing cracks. However wedging starts, it usually drives a fracture at a 90-degree angle into the surface. Along with the high-energy transfer, this means that wedging usually occurs at a distance from an edge, or if the edge angle is greater than 90-degrees. There is no better mode of initiation for large core reduction

known as the bulb of force. No other mode of initiation produces a conical bulb of force. The adjustment from Hertzian cone to bending or stiffness-controlled fracture leaves a characteristic wing-shaped or alar detachment from the platform. Since it takes a hard hammer to generate a Hertzian cone, it can be assumed that the alar platform detachment indicates use of a hard tool, like stone or very solid bone.

A ripple on the bulb of force represents a plane perpendicular to the effective direction of force. The plane of the ripple is almost always inclined from the direction of the blow. As soon as stiffness-controlled propagation takes over (when the bulb is deepest) there is a clear change in the orientation of flake scar ripples.

*Wedge detachment* - compressive impact followed by a split cone, primarily hard hammer, characterized by a plane surface.

because wedging can lead to flat fracture propagation. Although the fracture surface is nearly flat, you will often see concentric ripples radiating from the split cone.

Wedge initiation requires that the hammer be held firmly and the core be braced securely. Otherwise, there is not enough stress to develop a crack far enough to separate a flake from its parent core.

### *Bending initiation*
A flake starting from or near a sharp edge does not have enough mass to develop a Hertzian cone, so there has to be another mechanism for flake formation. Flakes start from sharp edges when force builds up enough to bend an arc of material away from the body of the preform or core. The arc develops a lip crack from one to ten millimeters deep before the fracture turns to parallel the face. Edges with sharp angles are subject to the most bending, and tend to have the largest lips when the blow lines up with the face. Outward blows have reduced

*Arcuate detachment* - bending action, primarily soft hammer, characterized by a diffuse bulbar swelling

lip remnants because critical stress levels build up so quickly.

Hard hammers can cause bending, but soft hammers transfer energy slowly enough that fracture is more stable. Undulations seldom occur in the region of initiation and adjustment from an arcuate (arc shaped) detachment to the rest of the flake looks similar to a Hertzian bulb of force except that it is less distinct. While arcuate detachments and lips do not guarantee a soft hammer made a flake, a preponderance of this form of initiation is at least an indication of tool preference. Indirect percussion blades are an example of flakes initiated by bending.

Rates of initiation influence flake stability. Sudden force leads to instability while gradual opening of a crack stabilizes its direction of travel. Soft hammers allow force to be delivered more gradually than hard hammers. However, this does not mean that bending flakes can only be made with soft hammers. Hard hammers can make bending flakes if they are used on ground edges, cushioned at impact, or used with a glancing blow. Damage to a hammer can eventually reduce its ability to transmit force so much it becomes, in effect, a soft hammer.

### Propagation
Propagation of a flake depends on energy reaching the crack front through stress waves or elastic deformation. The best way to visualize these waves is to think of them as the Raleigh waves you feel during an earthquake. Waves originating from a blow have long been understood as limiting how fast a crack can progress in elastic-induced fractures. A crack may grow only as fast as energy can be supplied. While lasers can provide enough energy to send cracks at

many times the speed of sound, and Raleigh waves can reach half the speed of sound, knapping speeds are far slower because high fracture speeds make fracture paths unstable. Waves that travel at higher speeds than the fracture only cause transitory effects when they happen to cross the fracture front. For example, faint features known as gull wings and Walner wakes can be used to measure the velocity of fracture in glassy materials like obsidian. The major energy needed for fracture is supplied by elastic deformation of the stone under load by a knapping tool.

Any deviation from an ideal fracture can be thought of as a change in how energy is supplied to the crack front. Cracks are most stable under external mechanical force (from the knapping tool) and unstable during release of elastic strain energy (from fracture, or tool damage). The better we can identify the nature of the change, the better we can describe the actions and tools of the knapper.

### Stiffness-controlled propagation

Stone used for knapping has the degree of stiffness which makes it possible to knap without the need for skill in controlling the direction of force. Skill is still needed in preparing the core and positioning the hammer, but nature has taken care of the really critical part. Compression caused by the flaking tool stabilizes the path of fracture, which follows a zone of critical tensile stress generally parallel to the core surface. As the fracture progresses, the stiffness of the flake so far detached tends to steer the direction of force in a way that promotes a long flake.

Long pressure flakes make the effects of stiffness most noticeable. Extra thickness on the surface stiffens the flake and turns its

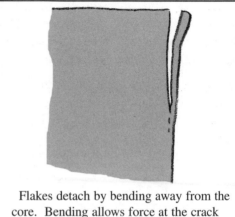

Flakes detach by bending away from the core. Bending allows force at the crack front to roughly parallel the face.

path into the stone. As the obstacle is passed, the fracture returns to its previous depth. Crack velocity is highest when force is aligned with the direction of the blow, and can decrease by half as the force inclines to 60-degrees. A relatively thin flake is controlled largely by stiffness, but is still under a combination of bending and compressive force.

As stiffness-controlled flakes lengthen, ripples increase in frequency, and sometimes in amplitude. This effect is likely caused by variations in flake thickness as well as by changes in load when the hammer or the platform suffers damage. The damage shows up as interruptions in the force available at the fracture front.

Computer models show that flakes on square edges don't want to progress as far as flakes where the outer corner has been beveled off. The reason is that the bevel improves the flexibility of the starting portion of the flake and feeds energy better to the distal end.

### *Compression-controlled propagation*

Flakes are rarely controlled entirely by compression, except in the case of bipolar flaking. Wedge-initiated flakes start in compression and propagate mostly in compression, especially if the blow is aligned with the fracture. Compression helps to stabilize fracture paths because it keeps tension from developing outside the plane of the blow. It has to do with the plane of tension being at right angles to the plane of compression.

The path of compression-controlled propagation is very stable. Because of this, undulations should be least pronounced in compression-controlled fracture, but the lack of undulations cannot be taken as an indication of compression control.

### Termination

Flake terminations reveal how stable the fracture path is. If the fracture path wavers, it is because the inherent stability of the stone is trying to correct an imbalance of forces. Often, the nature of the imbalance can lead you to better understand flint-knapping.

*Step terminations* are where the primary fracture plane stops without changing trajectory. They are caused by crack arrest, by lack of energy, or when a flaw is encountered--then outward forces snap the flake off by bending. Buckling also causes step termination if the flake is very thin relative to its length.

*Feathered terminations* are ideal continuations of stiffness-controlled propagation, where the fracture plane reaches the surface at a low angle. They indicate that control has been maintained throughout the flake removal.

*Hinge terminations* rotate strongly to the surface because of a sharp drop in fracture velocity, which allows the outward component of force to take over. When flakes flare on flat surfaces, the loss of energy often causes a hinge.

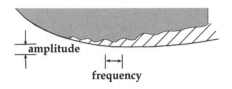

amplitude

frequency

*Undulated terminations* reflect force imbalances. The problem can arise from damage to platform, tool, or both.

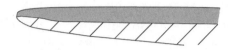

*Axial terminations*, where fracture meets the contact with an anvil without changing direction, are natural outcomes of compression-controlled fracture. They show compression was not lost before the flake completed.

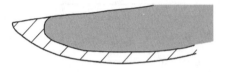

*Overshot terminations* rotate to the opposing face either because of excess bending energy or because the fracture is so deep that less energy is required for it to emerge on the opposite face.

A *plunging termination* can be caused when the flake approaches a sharp corner of the core (where stress is zero). Because the fracture cannot propagate in zero stress, it arcs into the body of the platform or core. Plunging is also caused by a high outward component of force.

inflex

retroflex

*Finials* are thin, fragile inflex or retroflex extensions of flakes due to crack instability. Large bending force or loss of compression can cause large stress zones parallel to the fracture. In effect, the fracture jumps from one critical zone to another. A surplus of energy is required for this feature to appear.

*Rising terminations* curve to reach the surface at a steep angle. Poor support of either the preform or the hammer causes this kind of termination.

## FLAKE PROFILES

Flake profiles and plans can be classified into a few basic forms that reveal much about the actions and intent of a knapper. Some examples indicate the information inherent in simple observations of geometry.

*Overshot* - tool contacts edge, severs opposite edge.
*Examples: contour, thin*

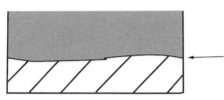

*Slab* - tool contacts away from edge, fairly uniform thickness.
*Examples: blank*

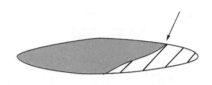

*Wedge* - tool contacts away from edge.
*Examples: Clactonian, shaping, edging, tool, blank*

*Face* - edge contact, carries thickness of bulb.
*Examples: Levallois, thinning, contour, tool, flute*

*Surface* - starts from edge contact, follows surface, and feathers.
*Examples: contour, thin*

## Flake plans

*Expanding* - pull mode.
*Examples: edge, shape, contour*

*Serial* - one full edge is the trough of a previous flake.
*Examples: edge, sewing*

*Parallel* - push mode or ridge controlled.
*Examples: edge, shape, contour, blade, tool*

*Crescent* - from notch or serration.
*Examples: edge, shape*

*Irregular* - shape is determined by previous flake ridges.
*Examples: contour, thin*

*Scalar* - small, thin overlapping flakes, often from shearing action.
*Examples: edge, shape*

*Alternate* - two full edges are troughs from previous flakes.
*Examples: edge, shape contour, blade*

## FLAKE ATTRIBUTES

Archeological evaluation typically suffers from subjectively. Many attributes of flakes, however, can be quantified. The following list shows how archaeologists can gain insight into what early workers of stone had in mind by considering flake attributes.

•Percentage of scar area by category of
  flake
  - shows relative priority of flake category
•Number of flakes by category
  - shows effectiveness of strategy
•Flake shape
  - shows strategy
•Interval of flakes by category
  - demonstrates effectiveness
•Average reach across face by category of
  flake
  - shows strategy
•Thickness of flake
  - shows technique, reveals cultural
  standard
•Consistency
  - shows uniformity and skill
•Platform detachment shape
  - identifies tool used
•Dorsal ridge definition
  - shows strategy
•Platform facets
  - shows strategy, reveals formal practice

When you put this information together, you can decipher the set of rules that a culture played by. The next chapter lays out some of the systems that knappers of the Paleo-Indian period in North America used to create distinctive and unique projectile points.

*Chapter 9*

# ANCIENT SPEARPOINT RECIPES

Early man used each of the techniques, concepts and tools discussed so far. As members of each culture designed tools to satisfy their particular needs, they also got into the habit of making a tool the same way each time it was needed. Archaeologists take advantage of the tendency to identify which people were most likely to have left a particular style of tool.

Most artifact types were recognized and formally described before archaeologists knew enough about knapping to include information about the processes used to make the tools. Following such an incomplete description to knap a copy usually results in something that looks out of place when compared to the original artifacts. Only replications that follow the same steps of manufacture as the originals can match them under serious scrutiny. To that end, I am including a few step-by-step recipes for some representative artifact styles.

Evidence for intermediate stages of work leading to a finished product is scanty and can be interpreted in different ways. My tests for validity of replication are 1) Can I match debitage and artifacts exactly to archaeological findings? 2) Are the techniques simple enough for early man to have done as a habit? Keep an open mind while reading the recipes. New evidence is coming in all the time, to refine and sometimes change the conclusions already drawn. More than anything, I want you to appreciate the complexity and sophistication that are behind such elegantly simple results.

About 12,000 years ago, a distinctive spearpoint design spread across the breadth and length of the American continents. Clovis points, associated with mammoth hunting, are easily identified by hafting grooves, called flutes, which thin their bases. Some archaeologists take the fact

**91**

that no other artifact style is so widely distributed to indicate that no people were already in place to hinder the introduction of Clovis spear point. By the time Folsom points replaced the Clovis style, mammoths were extinct and bison were the game of choice. Folsom points had a greater portion of their faces sheared off by fluting. Near the end of the Paleo-Indian period in North America, Eden points were made with strongly defined center ridges and delicate patterned flaking.

## CLOVIS

Clovis projectiles paradoxically are too advanced to be the earliest technology in the Americas, but they have no apparent predecessors. Only in Solutrean cultures from France and Spain, 18,000 years ago, do we see any similar technology from an earlier time. Even if we could account for bringing the technology from Europe, there is still the matter of explaining how the process came back to life after lying dormant for a few thousand years and the introduction of fluting to boot. As fine as any later New World technologies were, at least we can see the patterns of development from one point style to another.

Makers of Clovis points reserved the flexibility to use whatever strategies were best suited to solve any problem they faced. The results appear to have been much more important than the means used to reach them. This hallmark, seen in each stage of Clovis manufacture, sets this technique apart from other Paleo-technologies. Regardless of how they were made, long thinning flakes, driven from the base of thick spear points, distinguish Clovis points from almost all other technologies.

High-grade stone would have been easy to obtain in relatively large pieces if no one else had exploited the quarries. Heat treatment didn't seem to be used at that time, but these guys went out of their way to get good quality, strong stone. It doesn't seem to matter whether a Clovis point was started from tabular stone or any other form, because they had such good command of the process.

Clovis knappers' special forte was percussion. Large, thin biface platters found in buried Clovis caches represent as sophisticated a technology as any made by later cultures. Examination of waste flakes, as well as large preforms, shows that edges often appear to be heavy battered. While experimentally duplicating the feature, I found that battering with a stone hammer makes percussion flaking easier. Small cracks driven into the edge are then easily ground with a hammerstone. As a result, the percussion flake detaches with less force than usual, because of the induced weakness.

Lightly tilting the preform against a relatively slow blow, struck with a heavy baton, allows large flakes to travel across the preform face. Unless you take special precautions, overshot flakes can undo your progress. Gentle, even support minimizes this kind of breakage.

Before removing a series of thinning flakes, you should bevel, batter, and abrade an entire edge. It requires only a minimum of blows to flatten the surface by spacing each blow against the edge so flake scars overlap only slightly. Often, only three or

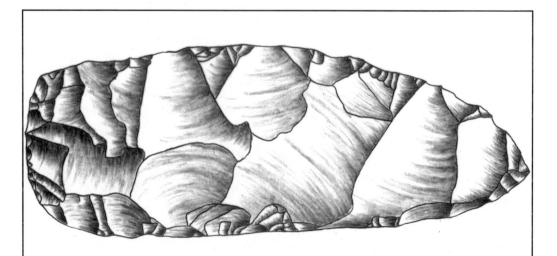

This Clovis preform from the Anzick site shows by its steep, straight lower edge that it was split from a larger platter.

four flakes can be enough to create a flat, even face. Because platforms are not individually prepared at this stage, it is common to see multiple impact sites for a single flake. Flake scars should reach almost to the far edge without heavy rippling. Next, set up a bevel for the opposite face. Once that face is flattened, the biface will have parallel faces and the thickness should be even for the full length. Repeat the process until the thickness reaches 9 or 10-mm. Shape is not an overriding concern for this first stage of percussion, although archaeological examples tend to favor broad ovals, resembling platters.

If platters could be made big enough, the Clovis knapper would probably split a section off when he was ready to make a projectile point. Excellent examples have been found at the Anzick site in Montana and the Simon cache in Idaho. The preform would eventually become a finished point after it had progressed through many stages of use. Until that final stage, the preform would have served as a chopper, scraper, knife, and eject-a-blade.

The next stage of percussion uses lighter blows on individually prepared impact platforms. Light support rocks against the blow, as before. As shaping takes place, the tip automatically thins. This stage shows considerably increased control and refinement. Before the tip is made sharp, the base needs to be thinned by driving a long flake, or flute, down each face.

In order to create this hafting channel, you need to carefully build a protrusion for striking a flute. The striking platform is set far from the center plane when a very long flute is wanted, and close to the center plane when the Western tradition of short flutes is followed. The impact site should also be isolated from the edge so the blow can only land on the platform, otherwise you shatter the ears. Grinding the platform keeps it from breaking under the blow.

When the platform leads to a straight, even surface profile, a clean blow creates the channel. Only the slightest support of your finger is needed at the tip to flute a Clovis in the Western tradition—just be sure that the sides are free of restraint or you may learn how end shock breaks a point. The blow itself can be slow, with a fairly heavy antler baton. Use a tight grip to add mass, and relax your elbow to assure a crisp transfer of energy.

Long fluting scars seen on Eastern Clovis styles can be duplicated by using percussion against an anvil support or by punching, similar to Folsom fluting. The differences between styles probably reflect differences in hafting preferences. Long flutes create parallel faces while short flutes provide a convenient bevel at the base. Both faces are fluted in the same manner.

Some Clovis knappers liked to take a single, bold flake on each face while others preferred to use lighter platforms and take two or three flakes from each face. The channel need only reach as far as the spear foreshaft will cover, often no more than an inch. The angle of edge left at the base should expand evenly to each face, leaving about 26-degrees between flutes.

Pressure dressing can begin as soon as the flutes are finished. Thickness and shape have already been established, so you can keep pressure work to a minimum. Pick off ridges selectively by pushing off flakes perpendicular to the edge. Scars from pressure dressing should have parallel sides and feather smoothly at their ends.

Clovis points were made to kill mammoths. As wide as they are, they would have passed easily between ribs without hanging up. Sides usually run straight and parallel within an inch of the base. A compass arc to the tip defines the remainder of the blade shape. The ears are made rounded, and a smooth concavity is left in the base. Edges are very sharp and even, except for the hafting area, where grinding sometimes reaches into the basal concavity.

Bone foreshafts found in a burial at the Anzick site in Montana provide clues to Clovis hafting strategy. The shafts were cut from green bone so that a sharp bevel was left, onto which a matching wedge may have been fitted. Casts of most authentic Clovis points solidly fit a reproduction of the hafting. Impact simply sets the point more firmly, without danger of splitting the foreshaft. Fitting the point to the shaft aligns it automatically and would take only the time to wrap sinew around the blade. A more recent socket tip of antler makes a good case for a hafting approach similar to that used by Eskimos. An Anzick foreshaft fits securely in the socket. In any regard, the edge angle of the projectile base seems to be important and fairly uniform among the casts examined. To reach vital organs in a mammoth, a spear had to penetrate very deep, through hair, hide, muscle, and fat. The relatively thin bone foreshaft would easily pass through the hole cut by a wide Clovis point.

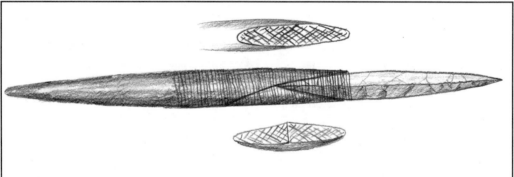

This system has been proposed for hafting Clovis points. The wedge-shaped piece has not been found archaeologically. Cross-hatching lets resin or hide glue stick better.

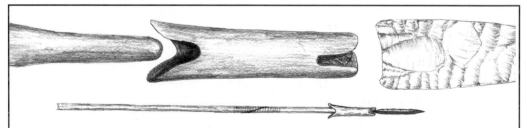

Found in a 7 to 8,000-year old Indiana peat bog, this hafting mechanism shows another way Clovis points may have been mounted. The foreshaft bevel is now simply a way to mate sections of the spear shaft. Drawn from Dennis Stanford, Foreshaft Sockets as Possible Clovis Hafting Devices, Current Research in the Pleistocene, Vol. 13, 1996.

## FOLSOM

After Clovis times, when mammoths were extinct, spearpoints were re-engineered to a most delicate form completely dominated by fluting scars. The game of choice was now Bison antiquus—a most formidable ancestor of modern bison. In spite of the quarry's size, the projectile tip was reduced to featherweight dimensions. We presume that changes in hafting caused the change in projectile point design. Since thinness and width were standardized, it appears that Folsom points may have fit as slotted replacements into standard foreshafts. Although some points were not fluted, most of them retain only a small margin of retouch scars bounding the flute. Thus, along with thinness, the flute is taken to be the primary distinguishing characteristic of a Folsom projectile point.

Folsom knappers choose the highest quality stone to make into projectile points. Strength and flexibility allow the channel flake to complete without collapsing or snapping. Control over flake trajectories is improved by selecting stone for fine grain and freedom from inclusions. It is sometimes necessary to use heat treatment so the finest flaking detail can be accommodated, without ripple or interruption.

At the earliest stage of percussion, you can avoid a great deal of effort by flattening a face that is already fairly flat. It is relatively simple to then flatten the second face. Following the Clovis tradition, an entire edge is beveled so flakes can be taken from anywhere on the perimeter by baton.

Using light support allows broad, flat flakes to be taken until a thickness of about 7 to 9-mm is reached. Scar terminations need to be feathered so there is nothing to interrupt the pressure stage.

Heat-treating is optional and can be used at any time before fluting. I like to use untreated stone to leave the projectile point as durable as possible. If the quality does need to be improved, my preference is to use heat treating after percussion. It minimizes rippled percussion flakes and snapped preforms. The stone only needs to be treated enough that sample flakes don't leave white tear lines at the scar margins. More improvement than that makes it too easy for flakes to undulate and for the prefom to snap.

Before fluting can take place, the surface must be carefully profiled to insure that the channel flake takes the proper path. Folsom pressure dressing can be most easily duplicated by specially preparing an anchor point for each flake. Paired bevel flakes provide a small spur that ensures the pressure tool is precisely and firmly positioned. Pressure is applied with considerable power parallel to the preform face. Flakes remove excess surface effectively and have nearly parallel sides. Bulbar scars from a single series of such flakes provide a lateral bound for the channel flake to follow. Viewed from the side, the face must be free of humps or dips, either of which can cause the flute to fail. A view from the end shows a hollow-ground effect caused by deep bulbing of the flake scars.

Folsom knappers sometimes went directly to fluting before working the second face. The practice has been called gambling on failure, but I prefer thinking of it as hedging the bet on the first channel flake by retaining strength. In order to get

One face of this Folsom preform is ready for fluting. The other face still has percussion scars.

sufficient thinning, thickness of the preform should be under 6-mm. If the preform is thinnest just short of the tip, the flute can break short without severing the tip by overshot. The tip itself is blunted and heavily ground to keep the force of fluting from shattering the point.

While faces are being dressed, I shape the sides in a gentle arc so the greatest width is in the center. Folsom preforms are often nearly the same shape at either end so they can be reversed if need be. It isn't a normal procedure, but examples have been found where Folsom knappers made this switch.

The nipple platform that carries the force of fluting is especially critical. Basically, it is a matter of beveling to the reverse face until the platform is very near the face to be fluted. Making the nipple too sharp promotes excessive bulbar scars. You should also avoid leaving a ridge on the back of the nipple since that allows enough

compression before fracture starts to cause overshot. A deep flake on either side of the nipple helps to keep the punch from dragging as the channel flake is removed. It isn't necessary to carry the flakes far, because a trough on each side is more important than a steeply defined central ridge. One test of a properly shaped fluting nipple is that it has the same contour of edge when viewed either face-on or end-on. Grinding and polishing complete the platform. It is common to see grinding on Folsom fluting platforms tending more to the face than on the extreme edge where the force comes to bear. This may strengthen the leading portion of the flake to insure it does not collapse before stress is properly distributed.

Surprisingly, a vise isn't necessarily the best way to support a Folsom preform. In fact, a vise sets up extra points of stress, which increase the chance of breakage. Since unfinished Folsom points usually have edges unsuitable for clamping, I designed a support system that works regardless of the edge treatment. A thin slab of stone braces the preform upright, while another slab serves as an anvil.

When the preform is in place, a rocker of antler can be used to punch the channel flake off. It is easy to hit too hard. A heavy blow can cause bounce, which usually breaks the point in half. The best results come from a heavy weight moving slowly. Don't make the mistake of forcing the blow because that will only cause overshot. An elk-antler tool found in the Folsom level at the Agate Basin Site in Wyoming inspired me to consider a rocker punch.

This is one way to flute Folsom points. It uses a rock brace and anvil, as well as an antler rocker punch.

After the first flute is removed, a nipple is beveled to the opposite face and a flute taken from the second face. If the point is still thick, yet another channel flake may be desired. Dressing is advised to even out the surface, but it isn't absolutely necessary. In fact, the second channel flake on a face makes an especially flat, wide flute when the first flute scar has been left intact. The reason is that the first flute acts as a column to feed force to the fracture front. The second channel flake behaves as two columns side by side. Compression rings change from a simple arc on the first flute to a recurved set of arcs on the second flute. Examples of multiple fluting are common in archaeological collections.

Once a thickness of under 4-mm is reached, no more fluting attempts should be made. Thickness occurs in a range from 2 to 5-mm, but the median seems to be about 3.75-mm. Measured between the scars, the same point may be only 2.5-mm thin. Ideally, both channel flake scars will match. In practice, not many Folsom points are found with mirror perfect flutes. In fact, many points are found with one or both faces unfluted.

There are other methods of removing channel flakes, in fact, experimenters have documented hundreds of variations. A good question is, "Why do you prefer this one?" My answer is that aboriginal flute flakes and scars have distinctive attributes of flatness, rippling, thickness, and so on. The rocker punch method seems to most closely match original results. My own methods have changed over the years as I keep finding different approaches. It is likely that it will be some time before we can say we know with assurance how Folsom points were really made.

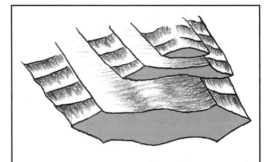

Effect of multiple flutes on Folsom points.

A full-length flute should break off in the low spot just ahead of the tip. If the preform is tapered too quickly to a point, the flute is apt to overshoot to the opposite face when the flute is as wide as the preform. Overshot can also occur when the platform has been made so sturdy that extra compression builds up.

Any surface remaining beyond the end of the flute needs to be removed by deep, flat flakes until the tip is not thicker than the rest of the point. This operation puts so much stress on a fragile platform that the tip is apt to snap off at the point of greatest weakness. Usually, that means breaking a preform at the termination of the flute. Archaeologists find that it happened to knappers in Folsom times as well. The problem is that the tips have been inter-preted as having been snapped off where the flutes ended—on purpose. If there had not been so many Folsom points found which extended past the flutes, the argu-ment might go on. This speculation about whether the tip is deliberately snapped off or not is important to the shape of the tip of the finished point. A rather sharp angle results if the tip can be salvaged in its full length. Otherwise, the tip is necessarily stubby. Repaired damage from impact causes the same effect, so most Folsom projectile points have a typically blunted look.

The shape of the preform should require only a minimum of retouch to finish the projectile point. Occasional examples of Folsom points show that when the shape is right to start with, retouch is hardly notice-able. Highly retouched points are invari-ably small, thoroughly reworked artifacts.

Delicate retouch is almost as much a hallmark of the Folsom culture as is thinness of their artifacts. As I have indicated, retouch can be viewed in the most literal sense. By the time the artifact was lost, it may have been edged many times over. My research has shown that a long, slender flaking tool with a sharpened point most nearly duplicates original retouch. The tool is seated on the sharp edge and given an outward flick to dislodge a slender flake. Each flake is only 1 or 2-mm past the last one, so the flake scars form a regular pattern of closely spaced parallel lines.

A good way to establish shape is to start with the ears. They parallel each other for about 5-mm and are 19 to 20-mm apart. From that point, the sides may swell 3 or 4-mm in a graceful arc to the tip. The widest part is generally forward of the center. A compass sweep from the widest point to the tip defines the arc. Archaeological evi-dence indicates that Folsom spear points

It is all too easy to snap a
Folsom preform tip during retouch.

were made up to 100-mm long (about 4 inches). The mean length, however, is only just under 40-mm because most points were reworked until they were discarded.

Before the point is ready for mounting, the portion of the edge between ears and midpoint is dulled—presumably for hafting. I have found that the easiest method for treating the edge is to use a small, coarse pebble to lightly rasp perpendicular to the edge. Any small projections are picked off and subtle shape adjustments can be made. Lateral grinding quickly adds the edge polish typical of Folsom artifacts.

## EDEN

Although fluting disappeared and many projectile shapes were used, percussion methods for making preforms remained much the same until the Cody complex came along. The earliest artifacts of this general style are known as Alberta points, followed by Scottsbluff and Eden points. Successive types within the Cody complex are separated mainly by pressure dressing refinements. This family of points is known for having square hafting stems, flaking that leaves a diamond-shaped cross-section, and a distinctive, straight central ridge.

While Eden points were made from a very wide array of materials, there is scant evidence of heat-treating. The stone used was often tough, but always uniform and free of flaws. Eden knappers were willing to work hard, but they did not waste effort on poor stone. The delicate patterning and slenderness of an Eden point disguises an unsuspected strength and durability.

Unlike the earlier percussion strategies that depended on creating faces parallel to each other, the Cody complex people wanted lenticular cross-sections. Another change was that every step of the process was more tightly controlled for uniformity than in other artifact styles. Multiple choice strategies used by Clovis and Folsom workers had no place with Eden people. By the time they reached the final stages of knapping, it was almost like making the same point as the one before.

The earliest stage of Eden percussion establishes a center plane edge on which every other step acts. At the same time, flaws are revealed and stripped away. Deliberate overshot flakes efficiently pick off opposite edges that are too square to work on directly. Platforms for the over-shot flakes are high above the center plane. Once the edge is established, however, all flakes follow flat trajectories originating from the center plane. Careful observation of workstations shows that most overshot flakes were later picked up and re-used to build end scrapers.

Before each blow, nipple platforms were prepared by pressure and lightly abraded. This guarantees the placement of each blow and sets up the same amount of stress each time. I get best results by holding the preform bare handed so the first two fingers are on either side of the platform. It takes some courage to get used to bare-handed support, but I am rarely cut. When the baton contacts the platform, it lines up with the fracture that is to take place, and the flake seems to shear off instead of peeling away. If the preform rocks against the blow, the flake will travel too far and cause a dip in the surface profile. When working against the center plane, both swing and support must be loose to avoid breaking the preform by bending.

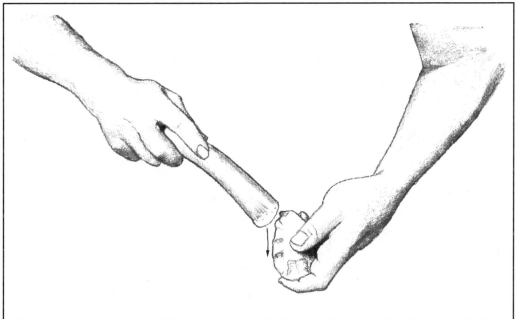

Here is the spectator view of Cody percussion. Hold the preform loosely without a pad. Stay relaxed; don't brace against the blow, and strike without muscle to develop a lenticular section.

Place striking platforms about 15-mm apart to mimic Eden preforms. The flakes will be about 20-mm wide. Flakes should travel in a fairly flat trajectory about two-thirds of the way across the face. Making the flake separation about 5-mm wide by isolating the impact site prevents excessive bending before the flake detaches. Work one face at a time until the thickness is between 6 and 8-mm and the width is about 35-mm. Eden knappers liked to make 100-mm long preforms, but anything over 50-mm will look okay. Preforms from the R-6 workshop site in New Mexico illustrate typical rounded ends.

Before patterned flaking can take place, the edges are given a double bevel by pressure. It isn't important to make flakes go to the center while beveling. Just make sure that no surface depressions reach the edge. Eden workers generally only extended their platforming flakes 3 to 5-mm. Holding the preform against a block helps keep all the flakes in the same orientation and to establish a plane face.

Final pressure dressing requires individual platform preparation. To begin with, a small spur platform is nibbled out of the edge. The presser is seated against this projection and the flake is pushed off. Examining the flake scar closely, you will see a weak, overhanging ridge. This overhang needs to be nibbled back to leave a square transition between the already flaked portion of the edge and the rest of the edge. The square corner can serve as

These typical Cody projectile preforms, excavated from the R-6 workshop site in New Mexico, show how controlled the process is, even at an early stage.

the next platform, or a small chip can be removed to isolate another spur.

Using a block support while flaking to insure a flat, straight fracture is the real trick to Eden pressure dressing. Either a hand-held or a table-supported block gives good results. A cutout channel lets flakes fall away freely without hinging or carrying across the median. Flakes are taken sequentially from base to tip down each edge of each face, with spacing as close as 2 to 3-mm.

Each flake having been removed with the same degree of force applied in the same direction, results in a faceted face. The facets intersect as a sharply-defined ridge running down the center of the point. A single series of flakes should be enough to make a good Eden replication. If the preform is overly wide, or the first series of flakes is not controlled, a second generation of flakes usually gives a sharper ridge, partly due to a lower width-to-thickness ratio and partly because there is less irregularity to overcome. The ridge effect is more noticeable when flakes are matched from one side to the other.

A well-flaked Eden needs next to no edge refinement. Lightly flick off the few ridges that protrude far enough to interrupt the profile of the projectile point. Short, delicate retouch flakes avoid ruining the patterned effect.

Final shaping tapers parallel sides gently to the tip. The hafting area is usually inset only slightly, and is about as long as it is wide. Normally, the haft is thinned by flakes from the side, to form a triangular facet at the haft base. Lateral grinding of the hafting area completes the Eden replica. Damaged bases were usually repaired by re-faceting from the base only.

## PARALLEL FLAKED POINTS

Parallel flaked points, which came into style following the Cody complex, used only a couple of slight variations in strategy. Instead of a steadying block, the preform was allowed to rock during flaking so the flake would arc over the center. The other difference was in using a clockwise sequence of flake removal.

Since shapes of parallel-flaked points varied quite a lot, many cultural traditions may have used the same technology through an extended period of time. Bases usually are slightly convex and edges sweep to the tip in graceful curves.

It is best that you think of these recipes as highly simplified recaps of very complex processes. So many attributes can be impacted by the passage of time, changes in stone, regional and individual variations, that virtually every artifact is unique. Few workshop activities have been recognized and described; even fewer have been shared with the public. By now though, you should start to see a basic pattern of human behavior. Humans have always been inclined toward stability and, once we learn that particular tools and processes work well, we tend to stay with familiar patterns.

Understanding an archaeological tradition is important, but just as important is the occasional abrupt shift to another pattern. What caused the shift? What remained the same? By answering those questions, we get to know ourselves as well as our ancestors.

The following chapter reviews how analysts decipher the ways ancient people worked their stone tools. Try to relate those insights to the few recipes we have just explored.

*Chapter 10*

# ARCHAEOLOGICAL ANALYSIS

The task of a lithic analyst is to decipher past events from prehistoric debris and relate them to a cultural framework. While experimentation suggests possibilities, there are more direct means of reconstructing the history of how an artifact came into being and how it was used. Standard definitions allow consistent descriptions of many features. When you can relate features of an artifact to the conditions that made the features, you have the means to describe the processes by which the artifact was made.

This chapter is intended to provide some context for the language of archaeological analysis. Unfortunately, many reports of the past contain much more information than appears to be needed to support the conclusions of the report. Part of the reason is that an investigator knows the story of a site is incomplete and it is important to convey some apparently unimportant data in the hope it will be useful later.

Analytical tools allow archaeologists and knappers to draw conclusions as to how Clovis, Folsom, Eden, and other artifacts were made. You can do it yourself—there is no reason other stonework cannot be largely deciphered. As you read this chapter ask yourself, "How can I use this information?" You may be surprised to see how much can be gleaned from thorough analysis of an artifact.

Since artifacts are made by individual knappers, each has its own precise shape, dimension, and topography. Certainly, there is a strong cultural influence and bias, but every result is unique. In fact, by definition, a culture is the accumulation of such individual expressions. Changes in cultures ultimately spring from individual deviations from the norm. While the differences may not have been recognized at the time, an archaeologist, at some later date, can define a break between two cultures.

It is challenging to figure out what the knapper wanted to do. Every artifact was made with some kind of standard in mind. Discarded preforms provide clues as to what deviation could be accepted or dealt with and what was abandoned. Other examples may show when a problem, such as a hump on the artifact face, was beyond the knapper's ability to correct and was accepted as part of the final result anyway. What is not wanted may still be acceptable. Recognizing the difference between a corrective action and one that was planned all along can be tricky. The "rules" of flintknapping are generally very flexible. For this reason, when attempting to reconstruct original criteria, it is important to examine a large sample of related artifacts.

## DESCRIPTION

Archaeologists try to recognize and define sets of knapping rules as artifact types. This can be misleading since many different cultures may have shared the same basic point type. Important distinctions between artifacts are made with clear and consistent physical descriptions. While the layman usually learns to recognize the difference between types by shape and dimension, many more aspects separate types.

Archaeologists describe artifacts very carefully. Metric measurements are usually used for consistency and to accommodate any resolution of accuracy. *Width* is generally measured at the widest part of the tool and at the basal constriction. Because tools have almost always been damaged and reworked, *length* measurements are biased to the short side. Rework also affects *thickness,* which is often expressed as a ratio to width because it is controlled to some extent by edge angle. The *width-to-thickness ratio* is also taken as an indicator

of the knapper's skill, particularly when it exceeds 8:1.

Formal descriptions of an artifact shape are sometime aided by using a compass arc. *Points of inflection* divide regions of different arc. Notches, insets or grinding can be used to define the *haft* of an artifact, where it was mounted to a shaft or handle. Projections adjacent to the haft, emphasized by notching or concave bases, are *ears* and usually serve to protect the lashing that secures the tool to a handle.

We often refer to the cutting portion of a tool as its *blade*. Unfortunately, European archaeologists use the word blade in a different context, to describe flakes that are more than twice as long as they are wide. Be careful of the context in which the term is used. Only deliberately long, narrow flakes should be called blades. Flakes that are long and skinny by accident should still be termed flakes.

Edges are rarely left un-retouched or without any modifications beyond removing major flakes. Trimming the projections and wavers is *retouch*. Retouch that causes a constant angle to one face is called a *bevel. Delicate retouch* straightens an edge with very little work and *extensive retouch* lives up to its name. Some edges are deliberately given a sinuous wave. At times, edges are given a propeller-like twist by reversing the direction of retouch halfway along the edge or by failing to keep to a plane. Portions of the edge are sometimes ground to avoid cutting the hafting or to protect the tool's user. Some retouch results from repair of damage, and may be spotted by an inflection in the profile or a change in edge angle.

## DIAGNOSIS

Diagnostic features that allow various knapping tools to be recognized provide a valuable adjunct to typology. Artifacts that bear a superficial resemblance to each other, but were clearly made by different techniques, may be given separate type definitions. When archaeologists investigate a site, they are interested in whether the artifacts found there were made by different groups. Often, each group used different tools and techniques.

A hard hammer that impacts a small area well away from any edge typically causes an initial conical fracture surface. Known as a *Hertzian cone* or *cone of force*, this special but familiar case of fracture is what you see when a small pebble strikes a pane of glass. As the conical fracture zone approaches the core face, it readjusts to a trough shape. This readjustment is described as a *salient bulb* if it is severe or a *diffuse bulb* if it is gradual. The bulb shape depends on the distribution of force and is called *conchoidal fracture* because of its resemblance to the shape of half a bivalve shell. Fractures caused by people are usually conchoidal. Those made by nature often take other forms.

All fractures begin perpendicular to the surface, even if only for a few microns. When the edge angle is sharp, there is a tendency for a *lip* to form as a pronounced adjustment of the flake trajectory. The lip is evidence of a fracture made by a bending action. A *soft hammer,* or *"pull mode"* pressure flaking, makes bending most likely.

Hardness of the hammer controls the shape of the part of the platform that remains with the flake as it detaches because of the differences in stress distribution. *Alar initiations* are wing shaped because they start as a ring fracture around a hard hammer impact and flare to reach the core edge. *Arcuate initiations* are simple arc detachments made possible because soft hammers transmit force slowly enough and over enough area that critical stress defines a trough rather than a cone.

The manner in which platforms are treated is often a good indicator of cultural norms. *Abrasion* serves to weaken some platforms by scratching the surface and to strengthen others by blunting the edge. *Battering* can also weaken edges, which allows flakes to come off with a relatively

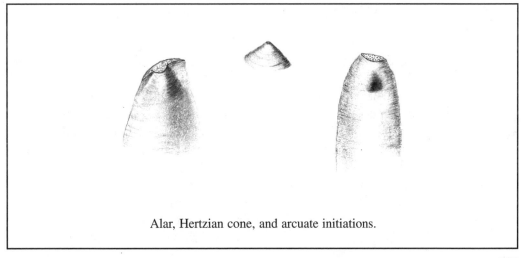

Alar, Hertzian cone, and arcuate initiations.

lighter blow. Deliberate flaking of *facets* of the edge controls platform placement and shape. Sometimes the edge is blunted by using the side of a presser to bevel the whole edge in a single, rasping swipe known as *shearing*.

An extreme example of edge modification, *isolation* of a platform ensures that force is applied exactly in the right place and is also concentrated to cause fracture to start easily. The isolated platform may also be referred to as a *nipple* or *spur,* depending on the relative sharpness.

Hesitations of fracture growth or other disturbances to the stress field cause the trajectory of fracture to waver. Relaxation of compression allows the fracture to veer toward the free surface. The greater the disturbance, the larger the undulation. Most often, follow-through of the knapping tool re-establishes enough force to drive the crack back into the body of the stone, where it progresses through a series of self-correcting changes in course. Known as *compression rings, ribs*, and *ripples,* waves in the fracture surface tend to become sharper and closer together near the fracture termination.

Stress oblique to the crack front causes visible shifts in the fracture surface radial to the applied force and perpendicular to undulations. The effect is most magnified near the edge because the free exterior surface influences stress direction. Fracture starts progressing in parallel tongues slanted to each other like the slats of a Venetian blind. These marks are known variously as *fissures, striations, lances, tear lines*, and *hackles*. The fact that tear lines are radial to the point of impact means that they can be used to locate impact sites that no longer exist.

Flakes are sometimes accompanied by a small, thin D-shaped *errailure* flake that peels off the face of the bulb, usually at a right angle to the main flake. The errailure flake often remains attached in the bulbar scar on the core. Buried fissures that develop laterally across the face of the bulb initiate the errailure. Undulations of the errailure emanate from the fissures that triggered it. Errailures may be useful in identifying relative brittleness of materials and may also help describe the type of tool used to remove a flake.

*Wallner lines* only exist in very homogeneous material, such as glass. Undulations are interacted with by shear waves generated when the fracture passes irregularities. Two sets of lines form convex to the direction of fracture. One of the lines is caused by reflection of the shear wave from the free surface. Measurement of the angle between sets of Wallner lines can determine the velocity of fracture propagation. A shallow intersection represents low velocities while high velocity causes the lines to diverge.

Fractures passing through imperfections often leave short, V-shaped marks, descriptively called *gull wings,* flaring away from the flake origin. Gull wings are a form of Wallner line caused by shear waves from the imperfection.

The meeting of two surfaces at an angle is called an *arris* (air-iss). Arrises are the most noticeable of all the features of a flake scar and, for this reason, are probably the most important. For meaningful definition of flake shape, special care must be taken to relate any particular arris to the most recent scar because flakes continually overlap each other. Fissure lines are usually evident along the edge of the last flake taken and identify their origin by pointing to the bulb.

Extensions of fissures sometimes occur as miniature flakes rounding off the usually sharp arris. The relative orientation of the arrises on a scar that has not been over-lapped highlights the distinction between push and pull pressure techniques. If the ridges diverge, a *pull* technique with outward forces is indicated. *Push* methods often produce scars with parallel sides, due to the alignment of force within the flake. An analyst has to be careful to check whether geometry of the core surface has more to do with flake shape than direction of force. The relative divergence of arrises causes a triangular area between adjoining scars. Pull flaking tends to leave large, triangular spaces due to their rapidly diverging nature, while push flakes usually leave little or no space between scars.

The behavior of a flake as it reaches the end of its travel tells an analyst a great deal. This is because the inherent stability of the flake weakens and force imbalances can take over. A *feathered termination* is a sign of forces kept in control, while a *rippled termination* indicates misdirected forces. If the compressive component of applied force is relaxed, the flake tends to rotate to the face in a *hinge termination*. An *outrepassé* or *overshot* is a rotation of fracture to the opposite face caused by extreme compression in the flake, usually due to high platforms or rotation resistance to impact. *Step terminations* are breaks in the flake where the flake trajectory stops on course. Such breaks are the result of tension caused by sudden outward forces, bending, or flaws in the stone. A series of step fractures is called a *stack,* and shows that the knapper has lost control.

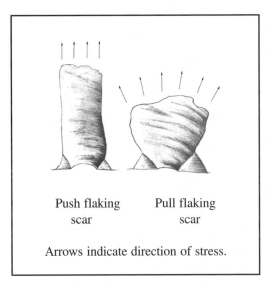

Push flaking    Pull flaking
scar            scar

Arrows indicate direction of stress.

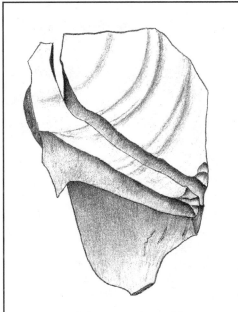

Overshot flakes are promoted by contact above the center plane, a guiding ridge, or increasing mass above the fracture plane. This example meets all three conditions.

A knapper's strategy reveals itself by the pattern of flake scar overlap. The work of an individual knapper can sometimes be identified by a unique, habitual flaking pattern. *Selective* flaking leaves an appearance that many people mistakenly take as random. If the overlaps are on the same side of each scar, then a *serial* flaking strategy was used. The direction of progression of flakes on each side is another aspect of strategy. Serial flaking usually results in the arrises trending the same way.

This is called *parallel* flaking, but can also be achieved with well controlled selective flaking. Flakes that slant across the center are called *diagonal* or *oblique*. If parallel flakes meet as a "V" in the center, they are *chevron* flakes. When they cross the center at right angles, they are *collateral* flakes. Spacing between flake removals is a very good indicator of individual strategy, both in dimension and regularity.

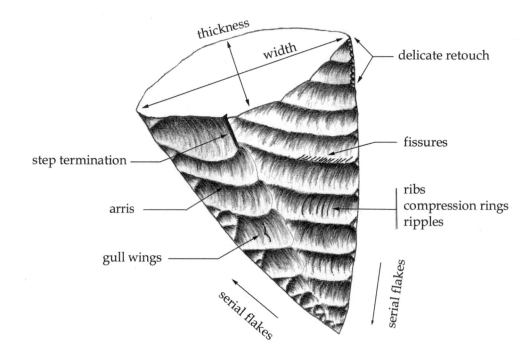

## BREAKAGE

Accidental fractures can be as useful to the analyst as those made on purpose. For one thing, they preserve an intermediate stage of work. For another, they give a clue to the activity that caused the breakage.

Thermal stresses caused by hot and cold temperatures can detach a circular *pot lid* to leave a crater with concentric rings around the center. This can represent heat-treating or it can be an accident. If residual thermal stresses are present, continued working can cause a break that is very erratic.

Impact fractures are caused when a finished stone tool strikes a hard object, like bone. Momentum helps extend a fracture away from the impact, but also causes shatter because of the follow-through. *Burination* happens when impact squares an edge by a splinter flake or spall. The sharp corners left by burination are so useful as tools they were often made deliberately. A sharp blow impacting the face of the artifact causes *radial* fractures. The result is a set of angular breaks radiating from the impact. Early man used deliberately made radial fractures as burin tools.

Indirect impact or leverage can cause *haft snap* from bending tension. The placement of the break can sometimes tell an analyst what kind of hafting was used.

*Bend breaks* result from mis-aligned forces and usually occur across the body of the preform at right angles to the direction of the blow. The break begins at right angles to the surface in tension, because of the low tensile strength of stone, and curves to the surface in compression. Blows on either end of a preform are especially apt to set up critical bending stresses. An identical looking break referred to as *end shock* is

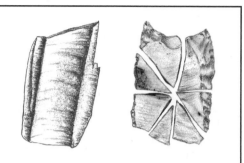

Burin tools can be made by spalling flakes from edges or by radial fractures.

caused by the force wave tearing the stone in two as it passes the point of support and sets up tension between two halves.

Blows that are too severe or incorrectly aligned cause *split breaks*. The fracture grows at an incline to both faces from the point of impact, and twists as it progresses. When it reaches the opposite side, it has the character of a bend break. The break initiates from a small dimple below the point of contact. My split breaks nearly always veer from right to left when I orient the broken preform with the impact closest to me and the tension face down (typical working orientation.) If enough examples can be recovered, it may be possible to indicate the handedness of a knapper.

Sometimes a preform will break in an irregular manner called a *perverse* fracture. This may be due to excess energy or just flawed stone. Too much energy can cause a fracture to branch in an effect very similar to radial fracture. On obsidian, the excess energy gives itself away in a *mist* of very fine fissures just before branching.

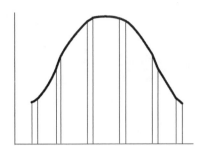

## DRAWING CONCLUSIONS

Although description and analysis of individual artifacts is indispensable, far more can be learned from a controlled collection, where we know more about the relation of artifacts to each other. The most obvious measure is the level of uniformity that was achieved. Sometimes this can be readily seen but, more often, statistical analysis is used to report a comparison with confidence. Special care is taken to select appropriate sampling strategies, specify degrees of variance, and establish significant correlation.

When a workshop site is located, it is possible to backtrack the knapper's process by *refitting* flakes. By reversing the order of flake removal, earlier stages can be reconstructed. Patterns and colors in the stone help, but the proper fit is easy to feel when it locks neatly into place. Strategies of flake placement and order are obvious when they can be physically traced. It is a good exercise to refit even modern work in order to appreciate the relation of a flake scar to the flake that was removed.

When archaeological *debitage* or *waste* flakes are examined, it becomes clear that many flakes are missing. Most of the lost flakes have been selected for further use as tools. Overshot flakes, for example, often have a shape suitable for end scrapers.

Other flakes, and even broken tools, can be found scattered throughout a site, representing a long history of reuse and adaptation.

Sometimes, it appears that certain stages of work were done at another site. The clues are subtle, but frequencies of occurrences can lead to understanding how tools may have been transformed into their final appearance over a period of time and perhaps travel. One way this kind of behavior is noticed is by *curation*. As an example, when I studied an Eden workshop site (R-6) in New Mexico yielded an extraordinary number of scrapers. At first, it looked like hides were being processed. Yet only two broken scrapers could be refitted to prove extended use on-site. The rest of the scrapers were of exotic materials and were generally worn out. Finally, I realized that while overshot flakes were very evident as flake scars, only a few examples could be found in the debitage. The conclusion was that scrapers were curated, or hoarded until replacements were guaranteed by the flintknapper. Further, certain kinds of flakes in the process of reduction were specifically designed to be converted into other tools.

By refitting debitage, we learn that many cultures had specific core strategies designed solely to produce flake tools. It is not always readily apparent whether spent cores were used strictly for eject-a-blades, but refitting them may help to recognize different uses for different cores.

The possibilities for researching collections of debitage have been only briefly explored. For example, were early people specialists or generalists? Can we identify the work of an individual knapper? Have people always had the present tendency towards right-handedness? By studying trading patterns and the distribution of artifacts, it is possible to deduce the importance of certain stone types.  In very early sites, we want to know how to distinguish human modification from natural agents.

Some of the terms I have introduced have little apparent significance.  As the study of lithic analysis progresses, I expect much less ambiguity.  Virtually everything discussed in this chapter has a huge potential for further elaboration.  The prospect of using an understanding of knapping as a window into past activities brought this book into being.  I hope you will also indulge your curiosity and contribute your own insight.

Refitted flakes on this Clovis replica show how the deliberate use of overshot flakes minimized the number of flakes needed to contour the surface of the projectile. Flake scars were traced to make it easier for you to match scar to flake. Note how each flake expands at a consistent angle—this helps you predict where the flake will travel.

*Chapter 11*

# TYING ONE ON

An experimental archaeologist naturally wants to put replications to use. Most of those studies are outside the scope of this book, including analysis of use wear, breakage patterns, efficiency, and energy budgets. Attaching artifacts to shafts can, however, aid in the appreciation of artifact design. When you try to haft a point to a foreshaft, the problems of tapering the base just right are driven home.

Since artifacts were usually mounted on perishable materials, we find fewer examples to guide us as we look at older cultures. Scattered remnants of surviving hafting show that artifacts were attached to handles with the same thoughtfulness and care that went into knapping stone. Weapons must be durable, effective, and easy to use. They must also be simple to construct and maintain.

For most of the Paleo-Indian period, it is easily inferred that some form of foreshaft was used for spear tips. Rather than carry an armful of spears, a hunter would keep a bag of foreshafts and plug in a new tip on demand. Early hunting was probably a communal event. When an animal was speared, the foreshaft stayed in, while the shaft fell out. As another hunter distracted the animal, the shaft could be retrieved and re-tipped in an instant.

Spears are difficult to throw by hand. A stick with a hook on the end doubles the energy of a cast by extending the distance through which force is imparted when the spear is thrown. Aztec Indians were still using spear casting boards, called atlatl's, when Spanish explorers arrived. The most persistent evidence for atlatl use is stone weights used to balance the sticks, and bone hooks that engaged a hollow in the end of the spear shaft.

Some unique foreshafts made of mammoth bone or ivory survive from Clovis times. About 8½ to 9 inches long, these shafts are usually pointed at one end with the other end cut off at a taper of 12 to 14 degrees. The flat part of the taper is crosshatched to provide friction and to hold resin. The question is whether the wedge fitted to the projectile or allowed mating to the spear shaft. Experiments with both systems may help in interpreting the evidence refered to in chapter 9.

Handles and shafts were primarily made of wood, although bone and antler were also used. Chokecherry was a favorite in the plains region, due to its availability, straightness, and strength. Other woods used include most of the hardwoods, willow, wild rose canes, and three-lobed sumac.

Starting at one end, with all shafts curving outward, arrow shafts can be straightened by tying them together in bundles of five. Remaining bends can be taken out by bowing the shaft after heating it over a fire or hot rock. Grease can be used to hold heat longer. Straightened shafts need smoothing, which is easily done by drawing them back and forth between two slabs of sandstone while turning the shafts. Further polish can be achieved by using fine knapping dust in a piece of leather.

Notches can be sawn with a flat flake of stone by using the flat face to square the outer sides of the notch. A modern expedient is to bind the shaft a short distance from the end and split the end open. The natural spring of the wood holds the tool in place, and the binding keeps the shaft from splitting along its length. This is where you learn that setting the tool into the haft is tricky. If one face of the tang is tapered

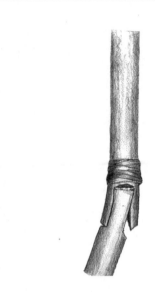

Green shafts can be notched by scoring and splitting. It helps to bind the shaft to limit the split.

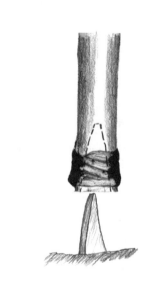

Shafts can be socketed by spinning them on a drill tip of bone or stone.

differently than the other, the point will not want to stay aligned.

There are some instances where notches are not desired. Tanged points, for example, require sockets in the end of a shaft. Cane or other hollow-centered shafts are helpful when they are available. If not, a socket can be drilled by twirling a shaft on top of a wedge of square-edged bone, or a stone drill tip.

The easiest time to work bone is when it is fresh or "green," while it is still somewhat soft. Boiling in water makes the bone even softer and pliable for shaping and straightening. Steep-edged flakes act as efficient push planes to shave the bone into shape. Just soaking in water easily softens antler. If the tool to be mounted has a small enough tang, it is feasible to merely force the tang into the pithy core of antler and let the antler dry. Early Europeans commonly scored a groove along the side of a pointed rod of antler so a series of bladelets could be set with resin. The same method was used to make sickles with antler handles.

Adhesives commonly glued tools in place. Resin or sap from trees or other plants is easily available. Gather it from fresh, sticky sap flows so there is still plenty of turpentine in it. Straight pitch is brittle, but you can introduce fiber binding by kneading in a bit of dung from an herbivore, like bison or rabbit. Repeated heating weakens the pitch, so you should warm it over a low candle-like flame. Wetting your fingers helps somewhat, but use quick, dabbing motions to keep from burning yourself. In places where tar pits and oozes were present, asphaltum could be applied like resin. Otherwise, boiling down tendons, hide, hooves, cartilage, and bones makes animal glue. The resulting mass of gelatinous protein can be immediately applied, or carried as a blob on the end of a stick for later use, or even eaten, when rations are low.

Binding a tool to a shaft will make it even more secure. Sinew is commonly used. Ligaments, particularly from along the spine, can be separated, stretched, and wrapped in place to dry and shrink. Sinew can be cleaned, dried, and later shredded or chewed to separate and soften it sufficiently for lashing. Rain can undo sinew, so it needs to be waterproofed with resin to make it usable in all weather. Rawhide can be cut in a spiral, or coil to get very long strands, which can be used somewhat like sinew. Soak it to soften for wrapping, and dry it in place. Rawhide is not very tidy, but it is excellent for binding large tools.

European mesolithic arrow points were wickedly effective, as this replica shows.

Cordage binding effectively avoids the limitations imposed by humidity on sinew and rawhide. Hair and vegetable fiber can be twisted to make cords as fine or as heavy as you want. The outer fibers on stalks of dogbane, milkweed, or stinging nettle make very fine yet strong cords. Some shredded bark works well but tends to be coarse. Leaves of plants like yucca have excellent, long fibers although it may take some work to separate them. Make sure that you use the same amount of fiber on each side of the twist and twist each side the same amount to get a straight, uniform string. The more cord you make, the better you will get.

When you use stone tools, you see that their nature influences the design of the handle. Stone edges cut readily with a sawing motion but take a delicate touch to avoid dulling or snapping the tool against bone. Short handles and short blades are more practical than stout handles and slender blades.

Resharpening, as the tool edge dulls, raises special issues. Should the mounting be dismantled or can the sharpening be done in place? What happens to the shape of the tool as a result of sharpening? How many times can a tool be sharpened and still be useful? I think you get the point. There are many things to be learned from firsthand experience with stone tools.

Yucca fibers make strong cord.

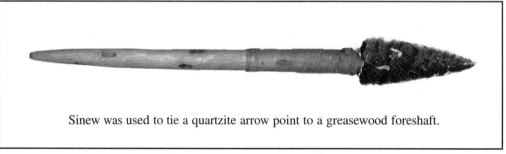

Sinew was used to tie a quartzite arrow point to a greasewood foreshaft.

In the following illustrations, you see some practical hafting ideas proposed by George Stewart of Windsor, Colorado. As a trapper, George tests his tools in everyday use. The key is to keep things simple.

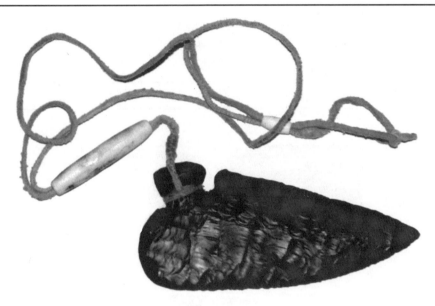

Here is an ingenious way to mount a corner-tang knife. When you are ready to use the knife, you simply slide the bone bead down to the tang, and use it as a stabilizer. The cord is tied on so as to not fray against the sharp edge of the knife.

Toe bones make effective short handles because they have a ready-made place for a security cord. Short handles are best for stone knives because you don't put so much twist on the tool.

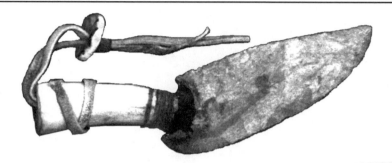

Another short handle looks attractive on a corner-tang knife, but it would be very easy to break the tang. If this kind of hafting were used, it would serve more as a stabilizer than as a sturdy handle.

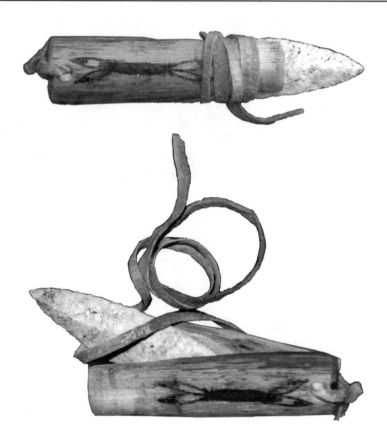

You can make a retractable-blade stone knife by splitting the handle and lining it with brain-tanned leather so the blade can seat securely. A strap of soft leather holds everything tight, and also provides a back-up cord for emergencies. When you travel, you can reverse the tool and protect the tip.

*Chapter 12*

# EXAMPLES

This chapter is a browse file of various flaked stone technologies that have been developed by people around the world. While some artifact styles are unique in place and time, most are duplicated or paralleled in different locations. Please don't consider the illustrations that follow to be a point typology. I prefer to leave classification to specialists. In every culture, some craftsmen excelled. The illustrations represent highly competent work, but both better and inferior workmanship can be found in archaeological collections.

It is difficult to gain access to museum-grade study collections that properly document where the collection was made and just what it represents. High quality casts of archaeological specimens provide a way around this problem. Many of the following examples were drawn from just a few of the casts available from the Lithic Casting Lab in Troy, Illinois. The first five examples represent transitions in the replication of a large Dalton point. They were knapped over a period of months by the author, with a cast made each time a new process was started. This kind of clue is most useful in archaeology. Seeing the change happening helps you judge whether a stage is complete.

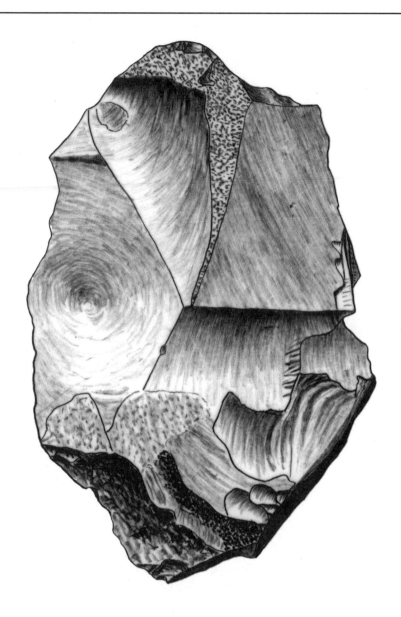

**DALTON quarry blank replica cast by Lithic Casting Lab**—thickness 21-mm

A palm-sized piece of tabular chert was selected from the Battle Mountain area of Nevada. The blank is flat, without twist, and thick enough to make a large Dalton. One flake has already been removed to sample the quality of the stone. Having been heat-treated, it fractured about as easily as obsidian. Normally, I prefer to do the initial percussion work before treating. While cracks were noted, I felt that I could work around them. Similarly, chalky deposits looked shallow enough to deal with. The planned strategy was based on methods used by the Cody culture.

**DALTON initial percussion replica cast by Lithic Casting Lab**—thickness 12.5-mm

The first priority was to get rid of obvious cracks and surface flaws. It was immediately evident that the choice of a heat-treated blank made work touchy. Large thinning flakes were made with extra care because fractures tended to undulate badly instead of feathering smoothly. A series of fractures buried beneath the chalk further complicated matters. Each platform was carefully isolated by pressure and ground to take the force of percussion without any chance of shatter. A platform was left un-struck on the right side. Its placement was planned to flake under or through buried cracks. The preform was lightly supported during percussion. Work was interrupted at this stage because the target centerline of about 10-mm had been reached.

**DALTON preform refinement replica cast by Lithic Casting Lab**—thickness 10.3-mm

I used percussion for the largest flakes at this step, but started with an antler tine to pressure off more of the irregular places. The buried cracks mentioned before are still present. Pressure work was done by traditional hand-held methods, using spur platforms for the larger flakes. Note that this stage is designed to regularize the edge and faces without more thinning. One edge has been beveled by pressure dressing with an antler tine to insure that patterned flakes can be taken later without running into surface impediments.

**DALTON pressure refinement replica cast by Lithic Casting Lab**—thickness 9.0-mm

The remaining edge was beveled and shaped to the outline desired in the finished product. A sequential series of flakes was taken from the right edge of each face, starting from the tip. After each flake, a small spur was prepared in line with the rear margin of the flake scar. Slight grinding insured that the spur platform was strong enough to carry pressure without collapsing. One flake has been taken on the left side, to continue the clockwise flaking pattern. The platform for the next flake has not been prepared.

**DALTON completed point replica cast by Lithic Casting Lab**—thickness 7.9-mm

Each sequential flaking pass on an edge decreased the preform width by about 2-mm. That amounts to just over a quarter-inch of width loss in the final dressing stage. Light retouch was sufficient to straighten the edge and shape the haft. Instead of indenting the base first and then taking long flutes, I removed a series of thinning flakes as I worked the basal concavity. The result is less of a fluting effect than there should have been. Since about a quarter-inch of the tip broke off during the final dressing, some initial beveling was required to reshape the replica. Continued use as a knife would damage the edge, and sharpening would always occur on the right edge of a face. Eventually, the long, tapered shape, with a propeller-like twist of most discarded Dalton points, would develop.

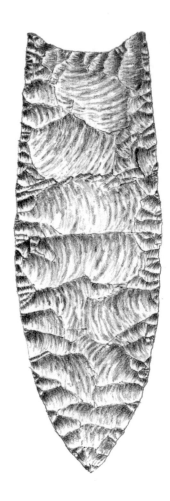

**CLOVIS replica**—thickness 6.3-mm

Only minimal pressure retouch defines the shape. Wide, flat flakes were knocked off by baton percussion. The flute was struck off while the tip of the preform was pressed against my leg. It is difficult to retain such wide, long percussion scars on the finished tool.

**CLOVIS replica**—thickness 7.3-mm ridge, thinness 5.8-mm scar

The extremely long channel scars on each face of this replica were made by the same indirect punch method as I use to make Folsom points. Baton percussion was used on Wyoming chert prior to fluting. After fluting, I used an antler tine to shape and trim the point by pressure.

**DANISH TRIHEDRAL replica**
thickness 8.2-mm

It is reported that Danish knappers started with a blade struck off the edge of a discarded, square sectioned axe. The three faces of this replica were flattened by antler pressure flaking on a blade of Normanskill chert. Then, a sharp tip of copper was used to "stitch" the center spine with alternating flakes. This kind of projectile probably fit into a socket and appears to have been designed for efficient penetration.

**PANAMANIAN TRIHEDRAL**
**personal collection**—thickness 14.6-mm

This three-faced projectile was roughed out by percussion. Pressure retouch flakes are sparse and deeply bulbed like the percussion flakes. These points were designed to make use of abundant cane spear shafts. All the hunter had to do was set the point in the hollow shaft and the spear was ready.

**AVONLEA POINT replica**
thickness 3.3-mm

Early archers in the northern Great Plains made these delicate arrow points from thin, flat flakes. I used a fine-tipped copper flaker to make this example. Indians would have used antler or bone. A tightly spaced, clockwise series of flakes created the regular pattern of scars.

**CORNER NOTCHED ARROW POINT replica**—thickness 4.2-mm

Light antler baton percussion was used to make a small preform of jasper. Pull mode pressure flaking was selectively applied to thin and flatten the point. Notches were made last by using a spatulate section of antler.

**CODY KNIFE replica**—thickness 5.6-mm

Although the Cody culture is known for its diamond-sectioned projectiles, the knives are flat and thin. Percussion with underpad support effectively flattened this piece of Wyoming chert. Minimal pressure is typical, as is selective bevel flaking.

**FOLSOM replica**—thickness 4.1-mm

After flutes were punched off each face of a Normanskill flint preform by an elk antler punch, a thin spline of deer antler was used for delicate retouch. Ancient retouch patterns could leave scars only a millimeter wide. Note the lack of obvious undulations.

**THEBES KEY-NOTCHED POINT replica**—thickness 5.6-mm

Widely spaced percussion blows uniformly thinned this Mississippi valley chert knife. Slightly doglegged notches were made with a copper punch. The edges were unifacially retouched by antler to make a strong bevel. This strategy makes the cutting edge plane with little effort.

**CALF CREEK KNIFE replica**
thickness 6.4-mm

Untreated Alibates chert was worked flat by baton percussion. A copper punch made deep, slightly expanding notches. The knife was sharpened and shaped by short pressure flakes. Continued sharpening would create a more typically seen angular tip

**JAMES ALLEN SPEAR POINT replica**
thickness 6.1-mm

When this style was used, some 8,000 years ago, parallel flaking was highly developed. I used baton percussion to make a preform of jasper. Long, regular push-flaked scars in a clockwise sequence give an appearance of carrying from edge to edge.

**131**

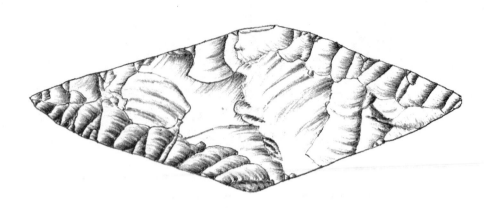

**BI-BEVELED KNIFE replica**—thickness 8.4-mm

This kind of knife starts out as a thin percussion oval and develops a propeller-like twist by repeated resharpening on alternate edges.  Normanskill flint from New York State was used in this example.

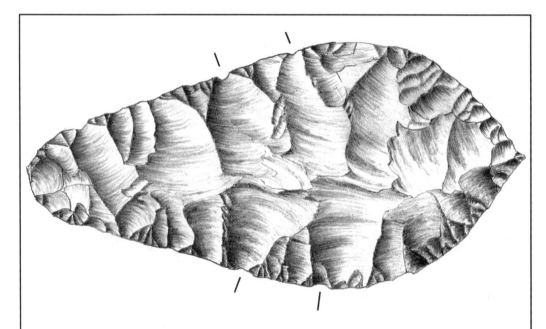

**BRITISH DAGGER replica**—handle thickness 9.8-mm

Short, fast percussion strokes effectively thinned this Normanskill flint from New York State. Bronze Age knappers of the Beaker culture used flint from the British lowlands.  Pairs of shallow hafting notches were often placed just below the widest part of the blade.

**AGATE BASIN SPEAR POINT replica**
thickness 7.1-mm

This artifact style almost never has any percussion scars left on a completed piece. A wide-tipped pressure tool was used for selectively flaking Wyoming chert so flake scars are wide with parallel sides.

**HOLLAND POINT replica**
thickness 4.9-mm

This Mississippi Valley style came from a heat-treated percussion preform of Crescent chert. A fine antler tip was applied to push off tightly spaced sequential flakes.

**EDEN replica**—thickness 7.4-mm

Widely spaced scars alternate from face to face and leave a wavy edge when seen from the side. An attempt was made to match flakes from edge to edge. The central ridge is well defined. The chert comes from the Hartville uplift area of Wyoming (popularly known as the Spanish Diggings.)

**EDEN replica**—thickness 8.3-mm

Flakes were closely spaced in a base-to-tip sequence down each edge. The scars are slender, with parallel sides except where a couple of flakes were taken out of sequence. The stone in this case is silicified volcanic ash from western Colorado.

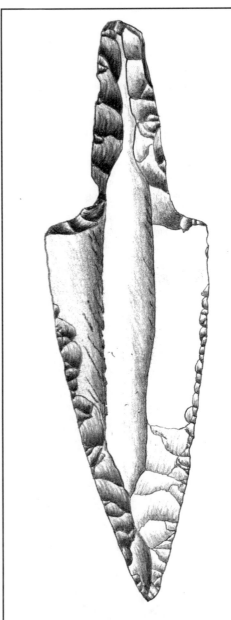

**HELL GAP replica**—thickness 8.2-mm

Antler percussion thinned this spear point of Wyoming chert one face at a time. The second face was worked until the target thickness was reached. Then, short pressure flakes were pushed off to finish the shape. This style was used to hunt buffalo on the high plains 10,000 years ago.

**MAYAN BLADE DAGGER cast by Lithic Casting Lab**—thickness 10.8-mm

This is an excellent example of using blade geometry to minimize the work of making a tool. Only a small amount of work was needed after the chert blade was struck off a core. A wood or fiber handle may have covered the tang.

**DANISH DAGGER**
**cast by Lithic Casting Lab**
thickness 17.1-mm

Rarely will you see such a complex combination of advanced flintknapping techniques. After initial shaping by percussion, this knife was ground, the handle was "stitched" using a copper tool, and the blade was parallel flaked by pressure. The stitching mimics casting seams on bronze knives of the same period.

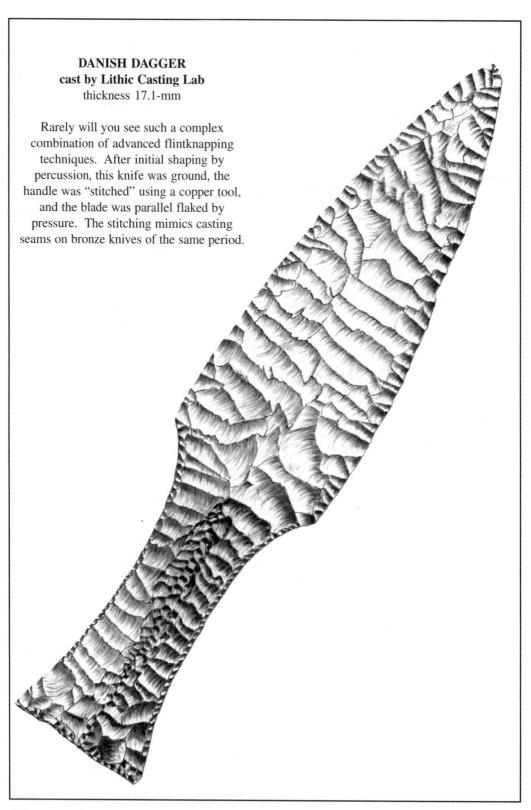

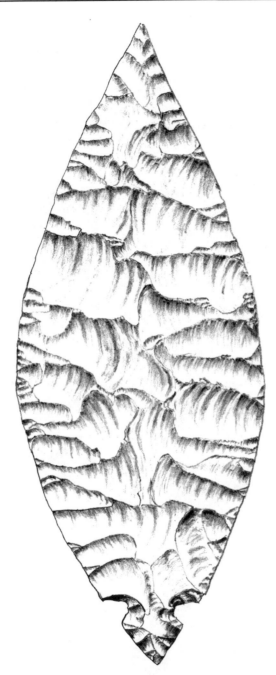

**TURKEY TAIL KNIFE cast by Lithic Casting Lab**—thickness 6.4-mm

This is a knife for show. Typically, cortex appears on each tip, the flint has showy patterns, and there is a slight twist in the edge plane. Highly controlled percussion was followed by minimal pressure.

**SWEETWATER KNIFE cast by Lithic Casting Lab**—thickness 6.5-mm

I have never seen an artifact with a higher width to thickness ratio than this flint knife from Texas. The flake scars are nearly all produced by percussion. Some ripples nearly reach through to the other face. Also note the narrow flake starts.

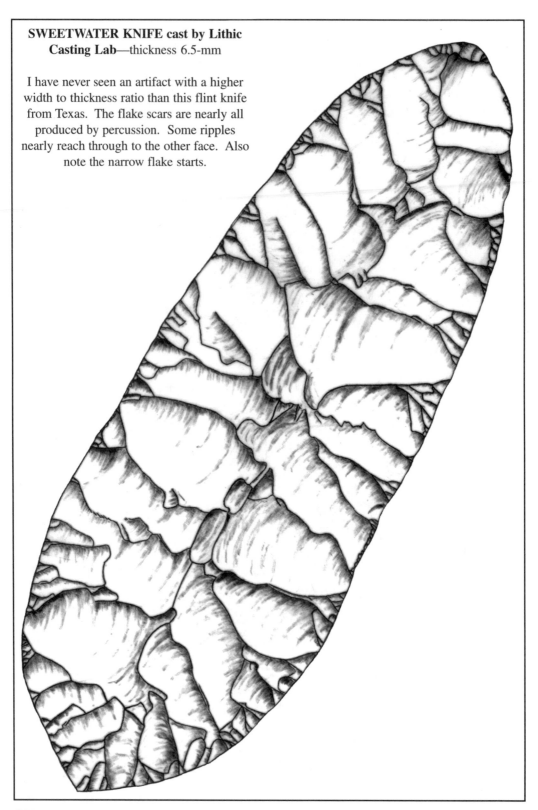

*Chapter 13*

# TIPS, POINTERS (AND OTHER DEBITAGE)

Flintknapping tends to be an untidy activity, so it should come as no surprise that I ended up with some bits and pieces that did not fit easily with the rest of the book. As with archaeology, some of the bits and pieces may be of as much interest as the rest. Here, you will find some helpful hints for learning (and teaching) flintknapping, as well as some sidebar digressions.

A good question we should ask ourselves is: "How did those ancient guys maintain their technical knowledge so well?" After all, they didn't have this book to help them. Part of the answer is that they did not have to teach all the little details. It was sufficient to impart some fundamental patterns that were inherently self-perpetuating. Look for some of those "basics" in this chapter.

## Ten suggestions for learning flintknapping

- To make good flakes, learn a technique first—then learn strategy, to take them from the right place. It will be necessary to learn more about technique after you understand strategy. Actually, it is a never-ending cycle.

- Platforms are of paramount importance. You cannot take short cuts in this area. Choose carefully and isolate well.

- For percussion—support must be loose. Delivery must be loose. Any muscle tension will rob energy from the blow and degrade your results.

- Do not attempt to make a flake that requires a quick increase in its thickness. It is almost always best to find an approach to the thick spot that allows a gradual thickening of the flake.

- Do not keep trimming edges as you work. It may look pretty, but you lose your best chances to get at the tough spots. There is ample opportunity to trim edges *after* the thickness and basic shape are complete.

- Get into the habit of drawing on the preform where you expect a flake to travel. Not until flakes happen as you plan, should you skip the pencil work. Even so, you should never stop anticipating where your flake will go.

- For pressure—keep the flake in compression until it finishes its travel. A most common error is to change the direction you are pushing before the flake has finished.

- If you do not have room for your pressure tool to follow-through, you will not be able to get a long flake. Keep the preform edge tipped up from its support.

- Impatience often gets in the way of success. Deal with problem areas only as quickly as is reasonable. Wait for the right opportunity to take a critical flake.

- If you do not know why a flake needs to come off, you are not in control.

## Percussion knapping strategies

In my efforts to create true replications—reproductions that re-create every step of the original process—I have learned several useful strategies. They are designed with primitive tools in mind and are presented in a rough order of priority for would-be experts to select from. The most important "rule" of flintknapping is that there are no absolute rules. There are also no guarantees, because some advanced knowledge of technique is required to make these strategies work to best advantage. I have observed, however, that many knappers are more in need of good strategy than of technique.

- Pick the flattest face and make it plane before working the other face. When you are ready to reverse faces, you will find that you have fewer problems to overcome.

- Prepare platforms with short flakes to minimize loss of platform sites on the obverse face. Thick edges allow sturdy flakes that travel without snapping off short.

- Do not worry about edges being wavy or ragged. Cleaning edges makes the preform look nice but takes away opportunities for platforms. This strategy will be most useful when there is little difference between faces of the quarry blank.

- Look for a ridge crest or arris leading from the edge to the thickest part of the preform. A blow directed along this ridge is the most effective way to bring the face contour under control. Once you have no obvious high spots, you should direct your blows at right angles to the long axis of the preform.

- Plan flake spacing to be as wide as flake scars. A helpful method for getting spacing right is to place a removed flake next to a flake scar. Expanding flakes make a flat, plane surface with a minimum number of blows.

- Wait until you have obtained the thickness you want before you pay much attention to final shape. Leave extra width on the preform so unanticipated errors or problems can be corrected.

- Strive for long, flat flakes right away. If the edge gets steep, it is difficult to control the contour of the face. Do not use this strategy if you want a replica with a well-defined center ridge.

- To emphasize a lenticular cross-section, you should prepare platforms near the center plane of the preform. Use a relaxed, freehand support and strike directly against the platform. Cody complex workers were masters of this technique.

- Avoid directing a flake so that it encounters increasing mass. Fractures tend to dive or step when the surface contour would require the flake to drastically increase its width or depth. A flake from the opposite direction will usually change the contour enough to make the flake you want feasible.

## Pressure knapping strategies

Knapping stone into works of art certainly takes a lot of manual skill and a mastery of technique, but that is still not enough. Good strategies make the difference between run-of-the-mill results and a masterpiece. A strategy is nothing but a conceptual framework for applying skills and techniques effectively. Some strategies are more important than others, depending on what you are trying to do. The following list is ranked in rough order of usefulness.

• Do not depend on pressure flaking to make major alterations in surface contour. Sure, it can be done, but there are better ways. Save your energy for creating effects.

• *Always* remove flakes from a properly prepared platform. Impatience is a great enemy. It is not speed that makes a good knapper, but the degree of control that can be achieved over each and every flake.

• The most uniform results are obtained when the initial surface contour is most uniform. Percussion, multiple series of flakes, or grinding can give you a good starting surface. Imperfections in the surface contour are apt to be revealed by ripples in the flake scar.

• Ideally, flakes should be thickest near the platform and taper to termination. The wedge geometry transfers force along the length of the flake with minimal chance of breaking off short. This means that you may have to sacrifice width by beveling in order to ensure successful flake removals.

• Spacing between flakes should not be too close. Otherwise, you can find yourself trying to flake in the trough of a previous flake. The most reliable flake removals are those which line up with the crest of a previous flake scar.

• Ranking flakes in serial order creates pleasing parallel scar patterns. If you move to the next platform in the same direction as the last scar slanted, you should get scars perpendicular to the edge. Flakes ranked in an opposite direction to the scar slant will create diagonal scar patterns.

• A simple shortcut combines the above strategies for making arrowheads. Shaping a flat flake into a preform by short flakes alternating from face to face creates a sturdy, sinuous edge. The crests of the sinuous edge serve as evenly spaced platforms for modifying either face.

• Retouch flaking intended to clean ragged edges or refine shape should be short and conform to the basic scar pattern. Otherwise, the pleasing effect you have worked to create may vanish.

• Patterned retouch adds to the overall aesthetic effect. This strategy works best if retouch is small relative to the major scar pattern. Egyptian Gerzian knives are perhaps the best example of patterned retouch.

## Folsom chert

About 10,500 years ago, a band of Folsom hunters camped near the Continental Divide in south central Colorado at an elevation just over 10,000 feet. Considering they were probably near timberline at the time, it was not a game-rich environment. The site was revealed in 1991 by animals burrowing in a terminal moraine. Because of the unusual setting, excavations were started at the Black Mountain site in 1993 to find out why it had been occupied.

Archaeologists noted a rich variety of cherts in various stages of point manufacture. Many of the cherts looked like those from known sources many miles away. Colors and texture were highly variable, leading to the impression that sources were widely scattered. Preliminary geological studies of the area failed to find local sources. It seemed these people were wide-ranging and carried raw materials significant distances. This interpretation was not unusual for Folsom sites throughout the Rocky Mountains.

Local cowboys had reported nearby chert sources geologists were not able to locate, even after searching several square miles. A fellow knapper, Larry Langford, and I did a ground sweep of the valley and found a wide range of local materials that had gone undetected. One of them was virtually *at* the campsite. Why had these sources evaded detection?

The answer is complicated. We found that while hydrothermal deposits of chert are scattered throughout the area, they are very localized and are not marked by obvious structural geologic cues. Further, they tend to be of such high quality that they do not survive long after exposure. Most importantly, glacial scouring had removed any loose evidence of the chert and subsequent erosion simply did not have time to scatter the remaining chert.

Since there were no camp tools, a picture is emerging of a band of males, exploiting the countryside. They may have been following game, or tracking stone traces in the glacial till. In any event, they were not constrained as we are by roadways and public access. When you are on foot and focused on a particular resource, it is not hard to find things, even in wooded or tundra-clad terrain.

This view of highly effective resource exploitation is important to archaeological interpretation. A small group of people can inventory an area for a whole spectrum of resources in a very short time. It is also possible to gather a significant quantity of items from scattered, sparse individual sites. We should entertain the idea that early inhabitants saw a richer, more prolific landscape than we see from the highway. Consequently, they needed to carry less from site to site than we often imagine.

For a flintknapper, realizing that chert of exceptional quality was widely available challenges the common idea that heat-treating must have been required. Heat-treating may only have become important in later times, when the best cherts had been high-graded.

## Division of Effort

Pivotal events redirect how we see the world. For me, a major pivotal event was to study a Cody culture workshop site that had been excavated by Dr. Dennis Stanford in the 1970's. It gave me not only a clear view of processes, but considerable insight into how the site inhabitants divided tasks among themselves.

Nearly the entire production sequence for making Eden style projectile points was represented at a site called R-6, located near the small town of Sapello, New Mexico. After quarrying hornfels from about three miles away, percussion was used at the campsite to reduce preforms in preparation for the pressure refinement stage.

It was reasonably straightforward to decipher the process of making spearpoints, but the presence of large numbers of scrapers was troubling. At first, it seemed that woodworking or hide preparation activities were done at the same time as the flintknapping. Signs of extreme wear argued for active use of the tools, but there were few indications of rejuvenation and hardly any scrapers were of the hornfels that was being made into spearpoints. Finally, I realized that an entire category of flakes was missing. Scars on bifaces showed that overshot flakes were favored at early stages of the process, but hardly any remained at the site. Once the knappers were finished with their work, someone had picked up the special flakes that would serve as scrapers. The old, worn out scrapers made of exotic stone were discarded and the group was ready for another expedition.

Once it was evident that there was a separation of roles, I saw other signs that specific tasks were portioned out to individuals. While percussion activities were spread across the site, the small amount of pressure refinement took place in a restricted area. In fact, most of the pressure work was on other stone than the freshly quarried hornfels. It isn't clear whether the divisions of labor were long standing or just convenient at this camp. Possibly, pressure refinement was deferred until previous points were lost or broken.

The people who made projectile points also made large, thin knives. The interesting thing about this is that knives and scrapers were sharpened with selective flaking, while projectile points were serially flaked. It is most likely, from what we know of anthropology, that men worked with hunting tools and women with the camp tools.

This site suggests that early people divided duties by both gender and skill. This is not to suggest that some individuals were incapable of flintknapping. It just says that when experts take over certain tasks, it enables the group to perform more efficiently than would be possible if everyone had to be completely self-sufficient.

# RESOURCES

## BOOKS

Forrest, A.J.

   *1983    Masters of Flint.* Lavenham,
   Suffolk: Lavenham Press Limited
   [Detailed account of gunflint making]

Helwig, Paul

   1984 *Flintknapping: The Art of Making
   Stone Tools.* Canoga Park, CA:
   Canyon Publishing Company [Basics,
   including pecking and grinding]

Waldorf, D.C.

   *1993   The Art of Flintknapping.* 4[rd] ed.
   Branson, MO: Mound Builder Arts
   and Trading Company [Pointers by a
   veteran knapper, well-illustrated
   booklet]

Whittaker, John

   1994 *Flintknapping, Making and Understanding Stone Tools.* Austin: University of Texas Press [Good academic
   summary]

McPherson, John and Geri

   1993 *Primitive Wilderness Living &
   Survival Skills.* Randolf, Ks: Prairie
   Wolf [Context for tool use]

## CASTS

Lithic Casting Lab, LCJ 577 Troy-O'Fallon
Road, Troy, Ill 62294 [First-rate casts of
authentic examples, great catalog]

J. C.'s Custom Lithic Casting, Box 304,
Granby, CO 80446 [Expanding repertoire
of Paleo examples, mostly from Colorado
mountain sites]

## INTERNET

Knappers Anonymous [Tip of the knappers
iceberg]

www.usc.ca/t64/links.html

The Center for Study of First Americans,
Oregon [Academic window into the past]

www.peak.org/csfa/csfa.html

## MAPS

U.S. Geological Survey, Box 25286,
Federal Center, Denver, Colorado 80225

**TECHNICAL READING**

Cotterel, Brian and Kaminga, John

    1987  The Formation of Flakes.
       *American Antiquity* 52(4) pp 675-708
       [The deep end of the knapping pool]

# GLOSSARY

Here are many terms that have been used carelessly, and some that are simply unfamiliar. To attempt some clarification, terms commonly used in place of each other, correctly or not, are cross-referenced.

**Aboriginal** Refers to primitive people, first inhabitants, natives. *See archaeological*

**Alar detachment** Wing-shaped separation from core. *See arcuate detachment*

**Anvil** Rigid support for a percussion blow.

**Arcuate detachment** Arc-shaped separation from core. *See alar detachment*

**Archaeological** Refers to evidence, connected to study of ancient people. *See aboriginal*

**Arris** Edge made by two surfaces coming together, specific type of ridge. *See ridge*

**Baton** Rod-shaped hammer, usually organic. *See billet*

**Bevel** Steep, wedge-shaped edge. *See bias*

**Bias** Preference, slant, inclination, prejudice. *See bevel*

**Bifacial** Two faces of a tool are modified. *See unifacial*

**Billet** *See baton*

**Blade** (European usage) Deliberate flake taken in a sequence, which is more than twice as long as it is wide.

**Blade** (American usage) Cutting portion of an implement.

**Blank** Article yet to be patterned (use as earliest stage, i.e. quarry blank). *See preform*

**Bulbar scar** Remnant on core. *See bulbous*

**Bulbous** Describes fracture path. *See bulbar scar*

**Burin** Deliberately constructed square edge used for a tool.

**Channel flake** Portion removed longitudinally from preform. *See channel scar, flute*

**Channel scar** Scar from channel flake. *See channel flake, flute*

**Compression ring** Well-defined waves on a fracture surface, of small amplitude and short period. *See ripple, undulation, rib*

**Debitage** French for waste flakes. *See waste flakes*

**Decortication** Removal of the weathered cortex, or surface of a stone.

**Diffuse bulb** Gentle swelling at the beginning of a flake. *See salient bulb*

**Distal** Terminal end, furthest from origin. *See proximal*

**Dorsal** The top face. *See ventral*

**Elasticity** Ability to withstand bending and return to original state without damage.

**Energy**  Capacity for doing work and overcoming resistance.

**Efficiency**  Ability to produce an effect with a minimum of effort.  *See reliability*

**Eject-a-blade**  My way of characterizing a core prior to its being exhausted.

**Errailure**  D-shaped flake often remaining on the bulbar portion of a flake.

**Extent**  Scope, limits, length.  *See reach*

**Flinder**  Stone splinter. (The only place in the book you will see this word.)

**Flintknapping**  Breaking flint, making stone tools by flaking.

**Flute**  Long, convex flake scar, usually longitudinal.  *See channel flake, channel scar*

**Foreshaft**  Short, tapered rod with a spearpoint hafted to it.  In turn, it is fitted by friction in the hollowed end of a spear shaft.

**Force**  The cause of motion.

**Gull wings**  Wing-shaped lines on a fracture surface that indicate interfering stress waves.  *See Wallner lines*

**Haft**  The handle of an implement.

**Hackle**  Irregular fracture surface associated with high velocity due to interaction between surface irregularities and stress waves.

**Hertzian cone**  Fracture form associated with a small projectile impacting a pane of glass.

**Homogeneous**  Structure is uniform.  *See isotropic*

**Isotropic**  Properties are the same, no matter which plane is observed, like glass.  *See homogeneous*

**Impact site**  Place where blow is to land, whether prepared or not, need not be isolated.  *See platform*

**Lenticular**  Cross-section like that of a magnifying lens.

**Method**  Regular, orderly procedure.  *See technology, technique*

**Nibble**  Remove small bites from an edge.

**Obverse**  Turned toward the observer, front part.  *See reverse*

**Outrepassé**  French for "over the edge."  *See overshot*

**Overshot**  Flake that rounds off the opposite edge.  *See outrepassé*

**Platform**  Raised surface, implies isolated character.  *See impact site*

**Point**  Something with a sharp tip.  *See projectile point*

**Power**  Rate of work.

**Preform**  Prior to final form (use where preliminary shaping has occurred.)  *See blank*

**Pressor**  Tool used to press flakes off a preform.

**Projectile point**  Sharp tip of something thrown or projected.  *See point*

**Propagation**  Extension or transmission through a medium.  *See travel*

**Proximal**  End nearest origin.  *See distal*

**Pull flaking**  Force causing flake removal is aligned outward from the flake.  *See push flaking*

**Push flaking** Force causing flake removal is aligned with the flake. *See pull flaking*

**Raleigh waves** The same kinds of particle movement waves associated with earthquakes.

**Random** Without plan. *See selective, serial*

**Rasp** Use a coarse stone to shear and abrade an edge in a percussion stroke. *See shear*

**Reach** Distance, extent. *See travel, extent*

**Re-create** Restore, to create anew. *See replicate*

**Reliability** Can be counted on, dependable. *See efficiency*

**Replicate** Reproduce something by re-creating every step of the original process. *See recreate*

**Reverse** The opposite or contrary, the rear of something. *See obverse*

**Rib** Curved ridge on a fracture surface, well defined. *See ripple, undulation, compression ring*

**Ridge** Raised crest on a fracture surface, meeting of two sloping surfaces. *See arris*

**Ripple** Small wave, short period. *See undulation, rib, compression ring*

**Salient bulb** Sharply defined swelling at the initiation of a flake. *See diffuse bulb*

**Selective** Chosen for special quality. *See random, serial*

**Serial** In sequential order. *See random, selective*

**Serration** A saw-toothed edge. *See spur*

**Shear** Nearly simultaneous removal of a series of flakes by pressing the knapping tool obliquely along the edge. *See rasp*

**Spur** Spine-like projection. *See serration*

**Surface isolation** Separable from the rest of the surface by virtue of raised topography and/or adjoining edges.

**Technique** Particular combination of tool and muscle used for a particular result. *See technology, method*

**Technology** Systematic and consistent application of processes. *See technique, method*

**Tranchet** French term meaning "cut-off."

**Travel** Act of moving from place to place, distance of a mechanical stroke. *See propagation*

**Undulation** Wavy surface, gentle wave with low amplitude and long period. *See ripple, rib, compression ring*

**Unifacial** Only one face of a tool is modified. *See bifacial*

**Wallner lines** V-shaped lines on a fracture surface, formed by interfering stress waves. *See gull wings*

**Ventral** The under-side, typically the flat side. *See dorsal*

**Waste flakes** Cast-off debris from flintknapping. *See debitage*

**Work** Transfering force from one system to another, measured by the product of the force and the displacement of mass in the line of force.

Mayan eccentrics combine exquisite knapping with artful representation.
See the four profiles in this replica?

# INDEX

## C

cache 20, 45, 93
calcaneum 30
Calf Creek knife replica 131
cane 117, 128
cast 95, 121
center plane 59
chalcedony 20-21
channel flake 79, 96
chert 20, 127-131, 133-135, 143
chevron flaking 110
chokecherry 116
chopper 94
Clactonian 56-57, 75, 77, 87
Clovis
  culture 59
  flaking 91–95
  flaking style 50
  point 105
  replica 114, 127
  tradition 96
  workers 101
cobble 54, 79
Cody
  complex 7, 100, 141
  culture 59, 79, 122, 144
  knife replica 129
collateral flaking 110
compression 38, 41, 49, 62, 80, 84-86, 108-109, 111, 140
  control 84-86
  stress 52
  wave 57
compression ring 52, 108
conchoidal 81
conchoidal fracture 107
cone of force 107
controlled fracture 38-39
copper
  hammer 28
  presser 31-32, 51, 128-129
  punch 30, 73, 130-131
  tool 68, 136
cordage 118

core tablet 77
core technology 54
corner notched arrow point 129
corner-tang knife 119-120
cortex 79, 137
crescent flake 88
crested blade 56, 57
curation 112
curved flakes 50
Cypress 10

## D

Dalton replica 121-126
damage 43, 80, 83
Danish
  dagger 32
  dagger replica 136
  knappers 52
  trihedral replica 128
debitage 77, 112
deer antler 130
delicate retouch 99, 103, 106, 130
detachment, alar 81
detachment, arcuate 83
diagonal flaking 110
diffuse bulb 107
dogbane 118
dogleg notches 73
dolomite 21
dorsal 89

## E

Eden 100
  flaking 33-34, 50, 71
  point 92, 100–103, 105, 144
  replica 134
  workshop site 112
edge polish 100
Egyptian knappers 52
eject-a-blade 94
elasticity 18, 49
elk antler 97, 130
end shock 40, 94, 111
energy balance 37, 47

# MEET THE AUTHOR

Since he was a pre-schooler, Bob Patten has been fascinated with flaking stone into tools. That early interest grew into what can now be best described as an obsession with lithic technology. He balances a unique blend of unbridled curiosity, technical background, broad exposure to the natural sciences, and archaeology.

Bob started applying mathematics to fracture mechanics while studying Civil Engineering at Colorado State University in the early 1960's. While mapping topography with the U.S. Geological Survey, he got to explore a large expanse of the country—in as much detail as the local inhabitants. It was a great opportunity to exercise a boundless interest in the land; what lay in it as well as on it, whether artifacts, fossil, or rocks. Seeing the landscape up close helped him immensely in relating to how early inhabitants had to cope with very different environments. Fortunately, Bob made contacts with

archaeologists, at the Smithsonian and elsewhere, who introduced him to physical and inferred findings that fit into his developing experience with chipping stone.

Over time, Bob replaced his rational, engineering approach to flintknapping with a growing appreciation of how our inborn intuitive capacity enables us to flake stone to our demands. Bob has applied himself most strongly to the technologies of the Paleo-Indian period of Western North America.

In 1990, NOVA included footage of Bob knapping a Clovis spearpoint in the program, *The Search for the First Americans*. Lately, he is working on a collaborative effort to decipher Folsom technology.

Bob is happiest when he is exploring some new aspect of knapping and doesn't like to worry about commercial deadlines and specifications. Since he demonstrates at events around the country, you may find an opportunity to chat with him about flintknapping.

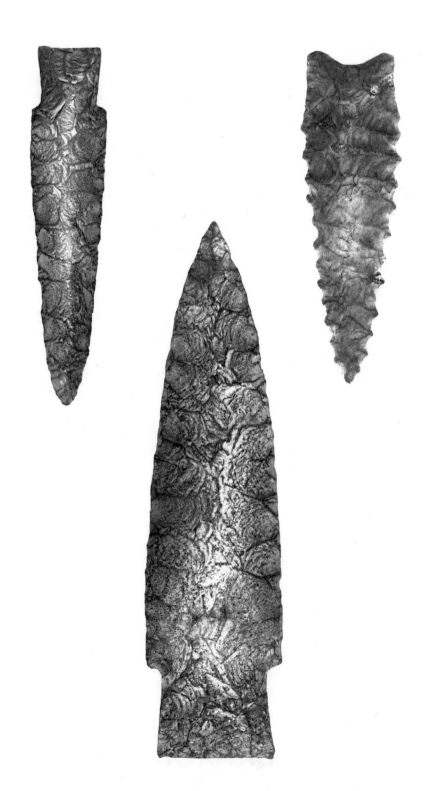

To order copies of this book, write to:

**Stone Dagger Publications**
**10803 W. Connecticut Ave.**
**Lakewood, CO 80232-4909**

Send $13.95 for each copy, plus $3.00 shipping
(Add 4.3% tax for Colorado deliveries)

Number of copies = _____

Total = $_____

**Ship to:**_____

_____

_____

_____